F.V.

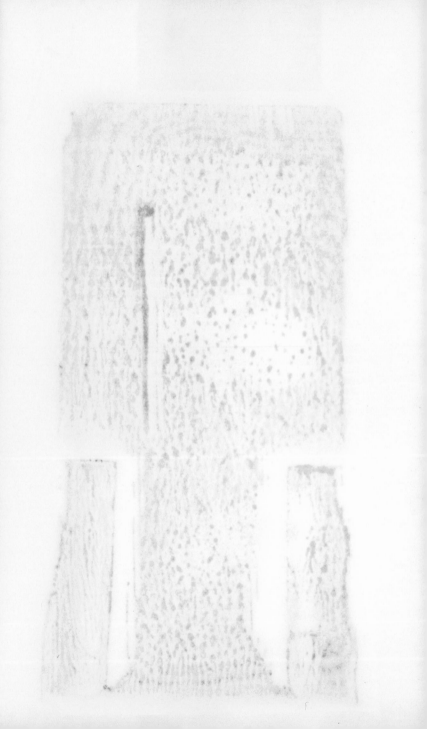

clearcut

Third in the Sierra Club Battlebook Series

clearcut

The deforestation of America

by Nancy Wood

Sierra Club

San Francisco • New York

For Brock Evans

The Sierra Club, founded in 1892 by John Muir, has devoted itself to the study and protection of the nation's scenic and ecological resources—mountains, wetlands, woodlands, wild shores and rivers. All club publications are part of the non-profit effort the club carries on as a public trust. There are 37 chapters coast to coast, in Canada, Hawaii and Alaska. Participation is invited in the club's program to enjoy and preserve wilderness everywhere. Address: 1050 Mills Tower, San Francisco, California 94104; 250 West 57th Street, New York, N.Y. 10019, or 235 Massachusetts Avenue N.E., Washington, D.C. 20002.

This battlebook is printed on Valentine Precycle Offset. The paper is manufactured from a nonwood fiber called bagasse. Bagasse is the residue that remains after sucrose has been extracted from sugar cane. The environmental benefits of using Precycle Offset are multiple: bagasse traditionally is burned (causing air pollution) or used for landfill in the wetlands of the Southeast.

Designed and produced by Charles Curtis, Inc., New York, and printed in the United States of America by Grafix.

Contents

Foreword

I had never seen anything like it before, nor since. Thick sponge moss carpeted the forest floor, with giant rhododendron and vine maple yawning over us. A green, still light filled the place, a bend at the corner of the river. We imagined we were wearing green glasses: every shade of green before us— lime, emerald, blue-green and gray, the light suffused and refracted in finding its way down from the canopy more than two hundred feet above. This was the glory of a climax Pacific Northwest rain forest: a river bottom of red cedar, western hemlock and yew.

From the moment I saw that place, I knew the true value of an old-growth forest. The only trouble was that I took it for granted. I thought this was the natural playground for hikers. I remember my surprise to find an old friend come wading up Blue River one evening into our camp there, fishing among caddis flies so thick they looked like fog hanging over the water. This was his natural habitat, too, or, more properly, the habitat of the rainbow trout that thrived there. But we liked to consider ourselves part of the habitat, and we reveled in the thought of being swallowed up in this green wilderness. The road was then ten miles away, and it wasn't much of a road. There was nothing but wilderness for twenty miles in all other directions, save for an old wagon trail to the east.

I knew this was in a national forest, but I thought then that this was the way the public's forests were supposed to be. I went away to college in the early 1950s feeling secure in the knowledge that all this would endure. Whatever other troubles the world faced, this was a constant—a place where things were right. But I was wrong. My faith was misplaced. I remember writing a college paper drawing an invidious comparison between the condition of private inholdings in the national forests—logged-off brush fields—and the virgin state of the public holdings in national forests.

The virginity was soon to be lost. By the time I finished college and had two years in the army behind me, I returned to find that what I thought was a constant was a perishable and expendable commodity. The forests of Blue River were being cut; the bend of the river was now the bed of a dusty logging road; and big, raw roads were going everywhere. All of the wilderness of the old Cascades was being logged. The blankets of Douglas fir forest that used to cover the serried ridges of these mountains were being punched full of ragged holes. Nothing—literally nothing—was being saved.

I felt deceived and cheated. Someone had been bartering off our national forests when my back was turned. At first I thought it was all some sort of monstrous mistake. These were the public's forests; after all, the Forest Service was committed to managing them "for the greatest good of the greatest number in the long run." This had to mean something more than stripping them, and Teddy Roosevelt, who set them aside, had said he hated a "man who strips the forests off the hills." But I thought perhaps the Forest Service officers, who were responsible, had been tied up by office work too much and hadn't gotten out to see what kind of places they were having logged. So I tried to get them to come and look; I begged, I petitioned, I protested; but it did no good. It was true—many of them had not seen the areas. But they didn't care.

The Forest Service had become a timber sales agency. Their business had become selling timber at the highest price, and the Willamette National Forest had the best timber left in the United States. Eugene was growing, and it was growing on timber, and the markets now were right, and there was no stopping them. The Forest Service felt its job was to provide the raw material to make it all possible, and it didn't want any cranky conservationists standing in its way. Progress consisted of logging trucks loaded with six-foot Douglas fir logs roaring down the highways.

To my consternation, I found that all the decisions had been made, and that for all practical purposes, they were irrevocable. Our custodians—the stewards of a public trust—had decided to sell off 99.9 percent of all the lowland rain forest. While it would not all be sold at once, all of this land had been earmarked for timbering. The allocation of national forest land to various uses had been made, and that was that. Recreationists could have the high country—that portion of it that was not good for pulping, grazing, or pumice mining; in other words, whatever part of it that was not good for anything else. The rich forests of the low country now belonged to the loggers, and those sentimentalists who liked old trees would be lucky to find a screen of trees left even along the main highways and rivers.

All of this had been done suddenly at one point of time when so-called multiple-use management plans were prepared in the late 1950s for the national forests of the Far West. Without public notice, without one single hearing, without anyone but the loggers being consulted, every acre of the national forests was committed to some program of utilization. In most instances, wherever merchantable timber could be found that could be logged profitably at some time, it was allocated for timbering. And nobody even knew what we were losing. The plans were based on maps prepared from aerial photographs. No one saw what was scheduled to go until it was too late.

It took me some time to find out how this could happen, how the Forest Service could go so wrong. For a while I thought the Forest Service had become the victim of overpowering political pressures from the lumber industry. In Oregon, timber was money, the biggest source of it, and those who had it also had political power. But then I learned that Forest Service officials didn't act cowed or subverted. Instead, they were proud, almost defiant—"their" forests were the most important commodity in the state. Their belief in the manifest economic destiny of these forests caused me to look more closely at the men who were now running the service. I noticed that the old Progressives who came in with Gifford Pinchot, who had the old ideals, were all retired from the service by the middle of the 1950s. A new type had replaced them: "industrial foresters" trained by the forestry schools to maximize income from forest crops. These men were doing what they were trained to do—find a market for their crops. The only trouble was that these weren't "their crop." They were "our national forests." To the industrial foresters, however, it was self-evident that the highest value of virtually all these forests was as fodder for the mills. To argue to the contrary was to be incomprehensible, to be talking nonsense.

I looked back to Pinchot for help, for insight into how to recapture the old ideals. Back through the reports of the secretaries of agriculture, the reports of the chief, and the old *use* manuals, I was led to Pinchot's autobiography, his explanation of what it was all about. Beneath a windy self-righteousness, I then discovered the bitter truth about Pinchot: from the beginning forestry meant logging, and Pinchot's essential quest was "how to make it pay." Pinchot had the national forests set aside to be logged when it would pay, and he arranged with the timber industrialists to hold national forest timber off the market to improve the price for *their* timber. Supposedly, the improved profitability of their operations would allow them to practice good forestry, but of course few did. Once their own more accessible timber was cut, then the national forest timber would be sold to them for contract cutting. The final denouement of this scheme was unfolding about me. It had taken the timber men until the 1950s to cut out most of their own lands, and now they had turned to the national forests.

It had all been planned from the beginning. Pinchot had fought John Muir on establishing new parks in the national forest lands because this is what he had in mind all along. Rather than places for people, for wildlife, for beauty, where the lessons of ecology were respected, where timbering is subordinate, Pinchot waited until a way could be found to get the loggers in. The seeds of this thinking have produced our present disaster—where forestry in our national forests means a relentless effort to sell off nearly all marketable commodities on terms not too unacceptable to industry, and to let the public use the residue.

In the text that follows, Nancy Wood tells what the results of this policy look like around the country. Her description must be a call to arms—for the public to recapture control of its forests, to assert a new future for some of the earth's finest forest land, and to find new stewards of a public trust who can be trusted. We must begin all over again.

—*Michael McCloskey*
Executive Director
Sierra Club
San Francisco, California

Prologue

I went to the woods because I wished to live deliberately, to front only the essential facts of life, and see if I could not learn what it had to teach, and not, when I came to die, discover that I had not lived.

—Henry David Thoreau

There is poetry in high places where subalpine fir march in stately fashion up the canyon walls, skirting the talus slides and granite cliffs. The Engelmann spruce march with them, playing out at timberline where the white-bark pine is locked in deadly combat with the elements. Up there, where winter is eight months long and icy blasts claim those trees with only a tenuous hold on the rocky soil, the forest is forbidding. And safe. Ancient patriarchs, long dead, mark the ridges and the places where snow and wind have been unleashed with fury. For decades they stand erect and gnarled, dwarfs, yet giants in their ability to endure. On the floor of such a forest, there is a profusion of the dead and dying, the split-bark hulks slowly reclaimed by nature, marked with a blackened blast of lightning. Who knows when it struck. In the highest places that forests can grow, there is no sense of time. Only adversity.

Farther down, where tall-grass meadows wave in a cool wind and the forest of spruce and fir and aspen quietly com-

mands the landscape, there is a sweet and haunting quality—
like nature set to music. In the dark, thick forest fragrant with
conifers in the heat of the day, an ice-cold stream runs rough
and sure over mossy rocks and hulks of dead trees that have
fallen into it. A warm sun filters through the canopy in hazy
point-blank rays. Each bristle of the conifers glistens in the
sun—splinters of light, pinpoints of dew. The aspen leaves,
translucent and pale, nod in the wind and the light. White
trunks, alive with hazy sun, show half-mooned eyes where
branches have broken off. The light burns into the humus, the
diary of forest life, layer after layer of leaves and bark and
branches and cones and bristles decayed and turned over by a
million living organisms. The process continues year after year,
century after century. So that digging down one finds rich dark
earth—the result of half a dozen centuries of rot and rain.

A long-dead tree is almost back into the earth from which
it came, its wood fibers broken down and rotting in little
chunks that look hand-hewn. From this springs new life—a
tiny spruce, some delicate green ferns, a handful of mush-
rooms, a pale pink shooting star. Beneath the rotting log, there
are spiders, ants, earthworms seemingly harassed by sudden
exposure to sunlight, a mass of fungi, a sprinkling of mites.
Poking up through the humus are the tentative shoots of a new
conifer forest, barely one season old, an inch or so high, fragile
enough to be killed by a shoe, tough enough to grow there in
the strange half-light of a forest left to itself to live and die
through so many cycles, through so many seasons, through
the best and worst that nature has to offer. And yet they live,
these tall and noble firs in the company of aspen and willow,
complemented by a splash of Indian paintbrush and bluebells,
of mertensia and monkshood, penstemon and forget-me-nots.
A hermit thrush sings again and again. A squirrel chatters
from a tree that is his own. The dense brush parts and a young

doe and a fawn come to drink as a chill settles over the forest
and the meadow beyond.

It is here in this forest that all time is present, in a way that
is as inexplicable as the way a thrust of granite against a rich
blue sky renews the man who sees it. The forest stirs the
deepest chords in the human spirit. It is a thread drawing man
back to a time of primitive simplicity. It is an assurance that
civilization need not strangle and twist into something "useful." For in this forest, in this scheme of things, there are lessons to be learned. The feel of pitch on the hands and humus
under the fingernails, the sound of tree limbs scraping together in the wind, of rustling leaves and falling cones, the
smell of rich earth filled with life-giving decay, the appreciation of rain held on the slopes by a cover of plants and
grasses, the sight of a spider's web drawn between two
branches (the only straight line in nature, as Emerson said),
the merry stream running quick and clear, the subtle life beneath the soil, the nobility of one fine elk, the particular grace
of one tree different from all the others, the form of a fissured
rock from which a struggling fir miraculously grows, the finely
wrought sculpture of a dead tree without its bark, the mysteries
of chlorophyll and transpiration. All this is a virgin forest,
growing by itself without man to manage it or decide its fate,
a forest which has not yet been humbled, a forest which has no
"use" except to those who come to gain some insight from it.

And go away a little richer.

1

For many years in connection with its periodic reassessments of the timber situation, the Service has predicted a prospective shortage of softwood sawtimber and this is exactly what is facing the industry now and why it is turning to the National Forests as its own lands have been depleted of mature timber.

It is my feeling that the Forest Service has been, and is being, pushed dangerously close to the brink with respect to timber management of the National Forests. I do not believe in brinksmanship when it comes to depleting the natural resources of the United States.

—Dr. Edward C. Crafts,
former assistant chief forester,
United States Forest Service,
before the House Committee on
Agriculture, May, 1969

It is already getting late if we are to meet the ever increasing demands for timber by the end of this decade . . . If we were to begin now and do all the things we know how to do, we could make a substantial increase in timber growth and yield in the 1970's.

—Edward P. Cliff, chief, United States Forest Service,
before the Senate Committee on
Interior and Insular Affairs, May, 1971

We have the directive from God: Have dominion over the earth . . . replenish it . . . and subdue it . . . God has not given us these resources so we can merely watch their ecological changes occur.

—H. D. Bennett, executive vice-president,
Appalachian Hardwood Manufacturers, Inc.

1. Clearcutting:
A Scalped Land Policy

The American forest is a battleground. What is left of it.

On one side is the timber industry. Having overcut its own lands, it now seeks to raid the national forests where half the remaining softwood supply stands. On the other side are individuals from all walks of life who believe that the national forests belong to the people and who decry the fact that each year one million acres of wilderness fall to industry's chain saws. In the middle is the U.S. Forest Service, painfully aware that in practice timber has been given priority over all other uses, yet apparently powerless to regulate that industry or even to justify the strangle hold that timbermen have on the national forests.

Within this framework the struggle over the national forests and who controls them and for what purpose is largely a political one. As always, the bureaucratic structure yields to pressure from powerful lobbyists and powerful congressmen. It becomes bogged down with red tape and master plans which, while theoretically sound, do not work on a practical basis because there is neither adequate management personnel nor money. It loses sight of the goals it had in the beginning. In the case of the Forest Service, now sixty-six years old, those goals were not only to furnish a continuous supply of timber to the nation but to protect the forests, soil and watersheds as well.

The Forest Service has failed to render this protection. Although it speaks reverently and convincingly of multiple use, the service virtually ignores all other values when timber is in question. Recreation, wildlife, watershed protection are given sparse attention.

The Forest Service is adopting and implementing on a wide scale various forms of even-age management, or clearcutting. Under this form of so-called "sound forest management," an entire mountainside can be stripped of trees, thousands of acres at one whack, running as much as three miles in length and a mile or more in width. Such a practice has an enormously devastating environmental effect which includes soil destruction, stream siltation, and a stinging blow to the aesthetic sense. It is also in violation of the Multiple Use Act of 1960.

Aside from political and legal considerations, money is at the heart of the matter, for industry must pay a fee to the U.S. government for the privilege of removing timber from the national forests. With $312 million in timber receipts anticipated for 1971, and an increase of $40 million expected in 1972, the Forest Service is one of the government's major money-making operations. It is no small wonder, then, that the Forest Service acquiesces to the demands of the industry for more areas to be opened up to the sale of billions of board feet.

The latest demand is that cutting be increased on the 97 million acres of national forest catalogued as commercial timberland, a demand manifested by the Timber Supply Act of 1970. The bill's chief defect was its failure to recognize that the public lands, including 187 million acres of national forests, belong to all the people and not only to the loggers. The bill was defeated. Had it been approved by Congress, it would have reversed some sixty years of forest conservation policy by denying a place for any use incompatible with timber harvesting.

With the bill's demise, industry looked to the White House for authority to cut at least 60 percent more than the 13 billion board feet it was then allowed to take from the national forests. The concession was granted by President Nixon in his executive order of June, 1970. This directive achieved by fiat what could not be done legislatively—with one catch: Nixon did not request allocation of funds toward this end. So the forests may have a reprieve, dependent solely upon appropriations rather than environmental concerns.

If President Nixon, the Forest Service and industry have their way, increased cutting will occur mainly in those crucial areas called *de facto wilderness,* unroaded areas which are wilderness in fact but do not have the legal protection guaranteed by the Wilderness Act of 1964. The timber industry covets these de facto regions. They contain the greatest volume of old-growth, virgin timber, a commodity as precious to a lumberman as tall grass was to the first cattlemen who drove their herds onto the prairie more than a century ago and subsequently overgrazed and destroyed it. If industry is allowed to continue at its present rate of cutting, all virgin timber in de facto areas may be gone by 1980. With it will go America's last chance to add any more such acreage to the wilderness system—a system which should have within it at least two million acres of de facto wilderness now classified as commercial forest land. Industry vehemently objects to this proposed two-million-acre withdrawal from what it considers to be its very own 97-million-acre timber domain.

The manner of cutting in the national forests disturbs many observers even more than any projected increase in the yield of logs. Clearcutting is total cutting, whether a given piece of land measures 5 acres or 2,000. It is this practice which has caused fiery debates, congressional hearings, endless attacks on the Forest Service and industry—and a challenge to both to prove that clearcutting does not harm soil, water and the ability of the forest to regenerate in perpetuity.

As far as industry is concerned, clearcutting is the most scientifically sound way to keep the forest producing trees forever. Industry foresters say that they can get second crops of trees to grow faster and better once the land is stripped of its "century-old, dark, dank Douglas fir forests." They insist that the only way they can stay in business is to grow second, third and fourth crops of trees as rapidly as possible with the assistance of such deadly poisons as DDT, endrin and dieldrin.

Lumbermen use the clearcutting method because it is easier. Roads are put down and across creek beds because it is easier. When the second growth of trees is all lined up in even stands ready to cut, it is easier. When these fairly uniform logs reach the sawmill, it is easier. And after all, the lumbermen point out, clearcutting *does* produce more timber. In 1969, 50.2 percent of the timber taken from eastern forests was clearcut from only 39.6 percent of the area logged. In the western forests, 30.1 percent of the logged area was clearcut, producing 60.8 percent of the volume of timber. With statistics such as these, what does a little erosion matter? Or some siltation in the water? Or the side of a mountain that begins to take on the appearance of Viet Nam after bombing? Yet the timber industry and the Forest Service, while admitting that some mistakes have occurred in the process of clearcutting, argue that no real damage is done to the land.

The truth is that clearcutting is the most destructive tool ever applied to the American forest.

According to testimony at Senate hearings conducted by Sen. Frank Church (D.—Idaho) in April, 1971, the most severe effect of clearcutting is the disruption of age-old soil conditions in the forest, which could leave the land barren in less than 200 years. In his testimony, Dr. Robert R. Curry, environmental geologist at the University of Montana, insisted that "much of the American landscape, upon which we rely for water, enjoyment, mental well-being, wood products and foods is, I believe, doomed to the same fate that befell the great forests of Dalmatia under the Greek and Roman axes, the Cedars of Lebanon, and the once productive areas of the English midlands." He told the committee that forest soils are nutrient reservoirs that take tens of thousands of years to form. In many areas, he said, these reservoirs "are now being lost through faulty logging practices at rates *hundreds to thousands of times faster than their formation*" (emphasis added).

"Specifically," Dr. Curry said, "my studies indicate that on national forest lands in all areas of the United States except some of those in the Gulf Coast States, parts of western Arizona and New Mexico, Multiple Use-Sustained Yield is being patently and overtly violated in that yield is not, and cannot, be sustained beyond one to four cuttings, after which the soils of national forests will be unable to support merchantable saw-timber until replenished by slow, geological weathering in five thousand or more years."

The loss of soil nutrients through erosion and clearcutting, Dr. Curry said, threatened to turn many of the western states —as well as the northeastern states—"into permanently de-

forested scrub, and shrub-covered, arid hills just as was done
in Greece, Yugoslavia, Italy and Spain and the Middle East
by early residents of those areas."

The next worst effect of clearcutting is sedimentation caused
by erosion when logging occurs on steep slopes or upon unstable soils. Hurlon C. Ray, director of water quality for the
Pacific Northwest Division of the Environmental Protection
Agency, testified that streams in logged areas have been found
to contain 7,000 times more sediment than they contained before logging. Sedimentation from poor logging practices chokes
stream beds many miles downstream. This causes loss of natural stream vegetation and destroys fish habitat. Silt in the
spawning bed smothers the fish eggs, Ray said. And he added
that clearcutting also leads to greater spring runoff, increasing
the danger of floods.

What does a clearcut area look like?

Imagine the mountains, ridge after ridge of them, rolling
slopes of dark green conifers punctuated with aspen—an
emerald empire of stately trees against the severity of granite.

But now there are no trees. They have been cut down.

The slope in the foreground is denuded—not a single tree
remains nor a shrub nor a flower. It is 1,500 acres big, enough
land for a community of 15,000 people living on quarter-acre
plots. But no one could live there or would want to live there.
The land is scarred with roads and skid trails and landings
(log-loading areas)—all the necessary gouges performed on
a forest to get the timber out. It is ugly.

It is ugly on the next ridge where a thousand acres have
been cut over. And on the next where the clearcut jumps a
watershed and spans two slopes. It is an odd sight, this clearcut, done in clean lines right up to the next stand of virgin
forest, intact until a timber sale brings it down. Like so much
raw material put on the block. As if it were not a living thing

at all, this forest. And so, from a distance it looks as if it had been shaved. What is left—a checkerboard of trees throughout a million-acre forest—does not please the eye. And what is left looks as if it ought to come down too. To sort of put it out of its misery. What good is *half* a battlefield?

To cut the trees down on over 20 million acres or 30 million in patches of 10 acres up to 3,000, is bad enough in itself. And so are the gouges—running into the hundreds of thousands of miles—which the Forest Service calls logging roads. They crisscross the clearcuts as if laid out by a drunken engineer. They do not go anywhere—except to a sea of stumps. One main road leads out of the forest to the nearest sawmill. And when the timber is all gone, the Forest Service will say this road is for recreation. *Welcome to the Stumps Scenic Area. Choose your own clearcut at a dollar a day per camping unit.*

Clearcutting has spread like a plague throughout the nation —from the ancient hardwood groves of West Virginia's Monongahela National Forest to the fragile subalpine forests of the Rocky Mountains, from the irreplaceable redwoods in northern California to the magnificent Douglas fir domains in Washington and Oregon. Nor does it stop there. In Idaho, Montana, Alaska, the forests have been leveled, with the logic that *demand* feeds exclusively on board feet.

Clearcutting is also a profit-making tool for an industry whose profits are already at an all-time high. The Federal Trade Commission reports that the timber industry showed the highest gains of any industry in the United States in 1968. Profits rose 97 percent before taxes and 91 percent after taxes, for a total net profit of $635 million. In 1968 seven companies made new records for net income, with earnings per share up 50 to 100 percent. Georgia-Pacific's net profit was $76 million. In 1969 its profits were up another 19.7 percent. The company cleared $91,760,000 on sales of $1,160,160,000.

THE BIG FIVE
RANKED IN BOARD FEET

WEYERHAEUSER	1,887,000,000
GEORGIA-PACIFIC	1,686,000,000
BOISE CASCADE	767,729,000
POTLATCH FORESTS	564,167,000
U.S. PLYWOOD - CHAMPION	466,820,000

Increasingly, the timber profit is coming out of the national forests and other public domain lands. Reports from the U.S. Department of Agriculture (parent agency of the Forest Service) show that of the total volume of softwood timber cut in the United States, the percentage taken from public forests continues to grow while the proportionate take from private lands declines. In 1962, for example, the removal of softwood (pine, fir and other conifers) from national forests was 28 percent of the total volume cut. By 1969, it had increased to 30 percent. And the trend is certain to continue, for as the timber industry depletes its own lands and other private holdings, it will seek more logs from the national forests. In fact, it will *have* to in order to stay in business-as-usual (that is, pursuing business based on unsound forest practices). The distribution of softwood timber in the United States makes this inevitable. Private lands, from which 61 percent of the sawtimber was taken in 1968, then contained only 35 percent of the nation's standing timber inventory, while public forests, providing 39 percent of the logs, contained 65 percent of the uncut timber. (See chart on page 27.)

Though neither government nor industry will disclose how much of their inventories is in *virgin* timber, one estimate by a veteran forester indicates that industry owns or controls less than 20 percent of the remaining virgin timber in the nation. The rest is federally owned, most of it in de facto wilderness areas to which industry nonetheless may hold a key.

Industry claims there is a shortage of timber. There isn't. Nor is there an increasing demand for it, as industry also maintains. In 1960, the actual demand for wood products was nearly the same as it was in 1910, and the demand for raw lumber was actually *down,* though the population had doubled and the gross national product was five times higher. The per capita consumption of wood was 219 board feet in 1950. By 1968 it had dropped to 170.

Industry's confusion over the difference between *demand* and *need* was attacked by Arnold W. Bolle, dean of the Forestry School at the University of Montana and chairman of a special study committee which in 1970 sharply criticized the Forest Service for its mismanagement of the Bitterroot National Forest. At the Church hearings, Bolle said that the federal government's 1968 goal of building 26 million new homes by 1978 would mean a new home for half the people in the country, a projection he termed "unrealistic." Yet, flaunting this exaggerated figure as a demand rather than a need, the timber industry still insists that the Forest Service raise its allowable cut to stave off not only a "timber famine" but a "housing shortage" as well.

What industry fears is that such wood substitutes as glass, brick, steel and concrete will be used in home building to an even greater extent than they are now. Nonwood mobile home sales have soared, as have multi-family dwellings, which use only two-fifths as much wood material per family as individual homes. It is this fear of being squeezed out of the market that prompts industry to strive for more and cheaper wood—as the case would be if the national forests were open to even greater cutting. As a result, the very companies that cry "shortage"

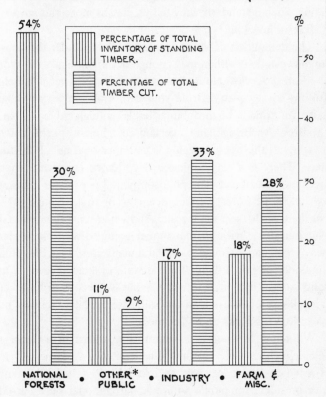

DISTRIBUTION OF SOFTWOOD TIMBER
BETWEEN
PUBLIC & PRIVATE LANDS (1969)

PERCENTAGE OF TOTAL INVENTORY OF STANDING TIMBER.

PERCENTAGE OF TOTAL TIMBER CUT.

54%
30%
11% 9%
17% 33%
18% 28%

NATIONAL FORESTS • OTHER* PUBLIC • INDUSTRY • FARM & MISC.

*OTHER PUBLIC FORESTS INCLUDE THOSE ADMINISTERED BY THE BUREAU OF LAND MANAGEMENT (DEPARTMENT OF THE INTERIOR) AND OTHER AGENCIES.

the loudest are the last to suggest that paper products be re-
cycled, that saw-log exports be stopped, or that the nation's
timber supply be conserved for the day when a true shortage
might loom. In all of their advertising there is an aggressive
message to *use more wood,* a message which also attempts to
convince the public that it is all right to cut down the forests
as fast as possible because this will satisfy our standard of
living. Such a standard, they tell us, means more and more.

But for how long?

The demolition of the forests is justifiable under the law—
anyone can do it with money enough to purchase a "sale" from
the Forest Service. No license is required. Experience is helpful but not necessary. Bring your own tools—a bevy of chain
saws, an armada of throbbing diesels, enough cables to hang
the Brooklyn Bridge, and a certain detachment for the task of
leveling all the trees. Logging is as impersonal as a blast fur-
nace. There is a single-minded devotion to converting those
trees into board feet. The philosophy that permeates industry,
as well as the Forest Service, seems to be that we have got to
cut the trees to save the forests. And what, it is often asked, is
America doing with all that timber going to waste in wilderness areas and national parks? Laments Bert L. Cole, commissioner of public lands for the state of Washington: "Our
solid base of income is forestry. What we need is to have certain classes of forest land set aside for forestry, so it is not
picked on for parks and wilderness."

William K. Moshofsky, assistant to the chairman of Georgia-
Pacific, echoes Cole: "In the Glacier Peak Wilderness, there
is a billion board feet rotting." And H. P. (Buck) Newson,
vice-president for public affairs at the National Forest Products Association, says: "We have to build some public back-
fire against the hysteria of setting all this land aside."

Right on, agrees Glen Youngblood, a Boise Cascade for-

ester who is associated with Outdoors Unlimited, a group of
alleged conservationists which opposes *any* further additions
to the wilderness system. "Outdoors Unlimited will continue
to promote the confrontation, not solve it. We will neutralize
the conservation effort... If it weren't for all those restrictions,
we could timber in wilderness areas. . ." (Footnote from David
Ainsworth, president of Outdoors Unlimited: "You cannot
preserve a tree. A tree is a growing organism.")

George W. Hess, manager of resource programs for Weyerhaeuser: "If you tamper with the intensive management process [clearcutting] you hasten the day when the demand will be
to open the national parks and wilderness for timbering. . .
There is a mystique in trees, an emotional involvement as opposed to cornstalks. We must set this druidism aside and
avoid emotion."

The timber industry ardently believes it has the right to log
off wilderness for another reason. As Julius Viancour of the
Western Council of Lumber and Sawmill Workers puts it:
"The inaccessible wilderness and primitive areas are off-limits
to most laboring people. We must have access and campsite
facilities. Otherwise it's just a paradise for a few of the very
rich. In this, it seems to me, the preservationists have cleverly
misled the mass of American recreationists. They have called
for lockup which actually denies access and use to most of us."

Viancour, however, does not deny that "most of us" still
know how to walk.

Another familiar industry tactic is to pick apart the philosophy of wilderness, as if anyone who believes in it is guilty of
irresponsibility, escapism, and slight madness. To freak out on
wilderness is to betray the productivity of an inexhaustible
resource. *Treason.*

Commenting on the Wilderness Act, the Land and Water
Conservation Fund Act, the Wild and Scenic Rivers Act, and

the National Environmental Policy Act, W. D. Hagenstein, executive vice-president of the Industrial Forestry Association, once wrote:

> These latter all have purpose statements which seem to deify environment as a sacred cow. They are popular acts because they reflect what most city dwellers think they want in the rural areas of the nation—a pretty playground to which they can escape from their own daily environment which they have been propagandized to believe is really unfit for humans. So they escape to a different environment where the practice of forestry could improve theirs by better housing, more conveniences, better watersheds, better wildlife management and a prettier countryside as a backdrop for every kind of outdoor play from picnicking to skiing. So now we've run the gamut from the beginning of applied forestry in the United States to the present public posture of environmental concern and widespread unappreciation of forestry.

Lest anyone wonder what contribution forestry could possibly make to the environment, Hagenstein had this to say:

> Forestry has always been an environmental undertaking. Its main thrust has always been taming the wild forest for Man's use and enjoyment by managing the ecology instead of letting it run rampant as though there were no people around.

Despite industry's protestations, wilderness use has increased markedly in the last two decades. One measure of this increase is reflected in the sale of backpacks. Twenty years ago 10,000 backpack units moved across the nation's retail counters. Last year the number exceeded 300,000. During 1964 there were 2,068,400 visitors to wilderness and primitive areas. By 1970 the figure had increased to 5,842,800. General forest recreation statistics are also revealing. Forest Service figures, based on a twelve-hour visitor day, show that in 1960 the forests had 92.6 million visitors, and that in 1970 the figure zoomed to 172.5 million. In some national forests, recreation income is fast outstripping timber income. Forest Service figures for North Carolina show that timber brings only two-thirds as much generated income as recreation. In the Chattahoochee National Forest, tourism generates 2½ times the income of logging.

Not all tourists are backpackers. Still, the forests and mountains of America are feeling the impact of outdoor recreation as never before. With 70 percent of the nation's 210 million people jammed into a scant 200 urban areas, and with more and more leisure time on their hands, Americans have a new yearning to experience nature and the land. But there is less and less to experience. Parks are crowded. In some designated forest wilderness areas, trails have been closed to prevent further erosion from the pounding of lug-soled hiking boots. Closer to the city, metropolitan open space is swallowed up at the rate of nearly 3,000 acres a day. In all of the coterminous United States, only 2 percent of the land remains in a wild and roadless state. Most of it is in the national forests, national parks, wildlife refuges and Indian reservations—some 55 million acres in all, or about one-quarter acre per capita.

One-quarter acre is not much. But it may have to be enough. Those who ask that the nation's de facto wilderness be spared the fate of clearcut logging do not seek more than this. They simply ask that a little land be left alone, for there is certainly enough space in this country for wilderness as well as tree factories.

Such a balance (if you can call a nine-to-one ratio *balanced*) may indeed be difficult to achieve in a nation committed to unlimited growth. The ancient and archaic attitudes toward man's relationship to nature still prevail. Indeed, they seem to

have changed but little in the century since Henry David
Thoreau observed:

> If a man walk in the woods for love of them half of each
> day, he is in danger of being regarded as a loafer; but if
> he spends his whole day as a speculator, shearing off
> those woods and making earth bald before her time, he
> is esteemed an industrious and enterprising citizen.

2.

Man is endowed with reason and creative powers so that he may increase what has been given to him, but up to now he has not created but only destroyed. There are fewer and fewer forests, rivers are drying up, wildlife is becoming extinct, the climate is ruined, and every day the earth gets poorer and uglier.

—Anton Chekhov,
Uncle Vanya

We abuse the land because we regard it as a commodity belonging to us. When we see the land as a commodity to which we belong, we may begin to use it with love and respect. There is no other way for land to survive the impact of mechanized man.

—Aldo Leopold

Blessed are the meek for they shall inherit the earth.
—St. Matthew

2. The Rise and Fall of the Great American Forest

The history of man has always been related to—and sometimes dominated by—the history of forests. Even the larger mammals could not begin to inherit the earth until, less than 50 million years ago, with the cooling climate, the hardwood trees began to flourish. And this occurrence led inevitably to one of the great turning points in the history of man itself. Toward the end of the last great ice age the spread of forests over what had been a subarctic plain forced a whole new way of life upon the fledgling human race.

Newborn out of the ice age, the primeval forest was luminous and supple. In the nobility and quality of its trees, in the number of species of bushes, vines and flowers; in the purity of lakes and streams; in the abundance and color of its birds and fish and in the personalities of its animals, no other forest that grew previously on earth could be compared with it. Its vitality was revealed in the way its trees evolved, for stony places and rich bottom land, for shady ravines and sunny hilltops, for south-facing slopes and north-facing slopes.

The forest flourished all by itself for nearly 50 million years. No one managed or improved it. Species lived and died. Land forms shifted. Whole mountain ranges were born. Glaciers melted. Forests spread until they covered the continent. Rivers formed. Climate changed. A menagerie of fantastic monsters nibbled away at what the forest had to offer. And mysteriously died. Not so the forest, which carried along through all those millions of years the seeds of trees we know today—the sycamore, the oak, the willow, poplar, beech, elm, mulberry and sassafras, the sturdy old conifers and the little trees of the rose family: wild cherry, crab apple, plum, mountain ash and hawthorn. Patient, strong, and spreading only with nature to manage it, the forest waited for man to come and live in it. And when man arrived, he brought with him the makings of its systematic destruction.

In North America, the impact of the Pleistocene nomad and early Indian was relatively light. The ravages of lightning fires, flood and disease periodically thinned the forests and prepared them for new growth. And nature's process of succession slowly converted the shallow glacial ponds and lakes into forest land—a process which continues to the present day in the bog country of the northern states.

To the first white settlers, the deciduous eastern forests were a terror, formidable in their towering darkness, teeming with savages and beasts. Sin lurked in the shadow of the oak and hickory. Soon the settlers cleared the trees to plant their crops. And the oaks became split-rail fences. As the emerging seaboard nation expanded westward, a greater need for wood developed. There were hearths to fuel, houses and ships to build. There were also, as Jefferson pointed out at the time, "great quantities of land to waste as we please," and the land included the vast virgin forests of the continent unlimited and unknown, stretching 1,000 miles west to the edge of the great grasslands.

When loggers began to cut their way through the New England states, the worst acts of devastation were often explained away with the carefree rationalization that the loggers were merely "letting daylight into the swamps." Nearly every man of that time believed that the only good tree, like the only good Indian, was a dead one. With the invention of the circular saw and the steam mill in the early 1800s, wholesale deforestation began in earnest. The wood-pulp process for making paper pushed the loggers even deeper into the forests, where tellers of tall tales empowered them with incredible strengths. Overnight a new folk hero emerged. His name was Paul Bunyan. Henry David Thoreau was not impressed. He merely observed that if loggers were tall enough they would surely attempt to lay waste the sky.

With cheap timberland and labor, and a small cash outlay to outfit a mill and start a log boom, timber as an industry assumed its place in the American marketplace. The deforestation which had begun in New England swept across New York and Pennsylvania, then successfully wiped out the vast pineries of the Lake states, and caught up with the yellow-pine stands of the South, the splendid Douglas fir forests of the Northwest, and the awesome sequoias and redwoods of California. Exploring these ancient sequoias in 1876, John Muir found sawmills "booming and moaning like bad ghosts, destroying many a fine tree." The specter of lumbermen cutting up the magnificent trees, thousands of years old, blasting them with gunpowder into manageable size, wasting half the timber and setting fire to what was left, prompted him to write:

Through all the wonderful, eventful centuries since Christ's time—and long before that—God has cared for these trees, saved them from drought, disease, avalanches, and a thousand straining, leveling tempests and floods;

but he cannot save them from fools—only Uncle Sam can do that.

Uncle Sam did nothing of the sort.

One year earlier in 1875, a report by the U.S. Department of Agriculture had this to say about what timbering had already done to the forests of the East:

Massachusetts—Scarcely a vestige of the original forest is left, even on the mountain-tops, owing to the demands of manufacturers and railroads.

Delaware—The best timber has long since disappeared.

Connecticut—Timber is being cut faster than it grows.

Maine—The pine timber has been shipped from the northern half of Penobscot until there is not enough left for home consumption.

Vermont—It is thought that the demands of the railroads will soon result in a scarcity of wood and timber.

New York—The mountains were originally covered with a heavy growth of hemlock, which was cut for the bark, the logs being left to decay . . . Complaint is made that many kinds of forest-trees are dying . . . The forests are being exhausted very fast.

Maryland—Within a few years a large number of saw-mills have used up the best parts of the forests.

Virginia—Since the war the indiscriminate destruction of forest . . . has been highly disadvantageous.

The dizzy cycle of boom and bust and cut and get out left in its wake a long list of horrors. Logger-caused forest fires consumed as much as 25 million acres a year and the burning of debris in forest after forest wiped out the seedlings that would have restored the ravished forests. The waste of wood was enormous: when the best stands had been cut, the stump merchant dismantled his mill and moved west, letting the deforested land go back into public ownership because he, having no further use for the property, declined to pay the taxes. The average life of a sawmill was twenty years, the length of time it took to strip the surrounding forest. As industry gobbled up whole forests, such towns as Bangor, Maine; Albany, New York; Williamsport, Pennsylvania; Saginaw, Michigan; Muskegon, Michigan; Eureka, California; and Portland, Oregon briefly boasted the title "Timber Capital of the World." There was enough wood for a thousand years, the promoters said. The stump merchants leveled most of the forests in a hundred.

The great giveaway of public lands between 1850 and 1871 created timber barons overnight and empowered timber lobbyists to push through Congress loose forest "homestead" laws which allowed even greater plunder by trespass and fraud. The General Land Office had neither men nor money—nor the wish—to prosecute timber thieves who, more often than not, were regarded as upstanding men in their communities. When the Homestead Act of 1862 was adopted, nearly 84 million acres of land were offered for unlimited purchase at $1.25 an acre. More fraud and scandal ensued. The continuing abuse of the land went on in a way best documented by B. B. Redding of the land department of the Central Pacific Railroad Company, who wrote in 1874:

> The Land Department at Washington does but little to prevent the destruction of our forests. It is rarely that a man is arrested for cutting timber upon Government Land. A system has grown up, under the rules of the Land Department, by which one or two men are allowed to file an affidavit in the local land-office that a certain tract of land is more valuable for mineral than agricultural purposes. Settlers are deterred from settling on it by reason of these affidavits; the land occupies an anomalous position; it is neither under the care of the settlers nor the

Government, and remains in this condition until all the timber and wood is stolen and sold . . . The loggers and shake-makers strip it of its timber, and the Government derives no benefit while the people are demoralized . . . I know of no remedy for this as legislation and the Land Department favor the mineral rather the agriculturist.

In every land law there were loopholes big enough to satisfy the most modest thief. Since the Homestead Act required that a dwelling be erected upon the site, frontiersmen put up "homes" as small as fourteen by sixteen inches. Under the Timber Culture Act of 1873 which offered 160 acres to any settler who could cultivate trees on 40 acres, the pioneer would happily cut down and sell everything on 120 acres. Others who obtained holdings under the Swamp and Overflow Act swore to the "overflowed" character of the land by describing how they crossed it in a boat, neglecting to mention that the boat was hauled by mule. The Forest Management Act of 1897 subjected additional lands to virtually unlimited prospecting and development of mineral resources in all of the forest reserves. This act opened the way to overgrazing and water abuse and allowed such huge mining corporations as Anaconda to take millions of board feet of timber and then to trade the devastated land for virgin territory elsewhere.

The states, not to be outdone by the federal government, offered priceless forests for next to nothing. The going rate per acre was 12½ cents in Maine and Pennsylvania; choice hardwood forests in North Carolina fell to the lumbermen at 10 cents an acre.

A few lonely voices spoke out—William Bartram, the colonial naturalist; Emerson, Thoreau, and Muir; Carl Schurz, secretary of the interior under President Grant, who called the timber barons thieves and urged establishment of forest preserves, reforestation, and penalties for fire-setters. He was denounced as un-American and against honest enterprise. Charles Russell, the noted painter of the nineteenth century West summed up the temper of those times:

> I have been called a pioneer. In my book a pioneer is a man who comes to virgin country, traps off all the fur, kills off all the wild meat, cuts down all the trees, grazes off all the grass, plows the roots up and strings ten million miles of wire. A pioneer destroys things and calls it civilization.

George Perkins Marsh, the land philosopher and farsighted conservationist, was more to the point. In his 1861 master-piece, *Man and Nature,* he wrote:

> The ravages committed by man subvert the relations and destroy the balance which nature has established . . . and she avenges herself upon the intruder by letting loose her destructive energies . . . When the forest is gone, the great reservoir of moisture stored up in its vegetable mould is evaporated . . . The well-wooded and humid hills are turned to ridges of dry rock, and . . . the whole earth, unless rescued by human art from the physical degrada-tion to which it tends, becomes an assemblage of bald mountains, of barren, turfless hills, and of swampy and malarious plains.

Marsh's book gave strong support to the advocates of a forestry program in the United States, citing the woodlands as the most endangered resource, urging reforestation and a na-tional program of experimental forestry. Unfortunately, woodsmen were too busy felling trees to pay him any attention. It was not until 1877, when Carl Schurz, a crusading senator from Wisconsin, was appointed secretary of the interior by Rutherford Hayes, that the first real attempt to crack down on the timber industry began. Schurz's first act as secretary was to order an intensive study of forest depredations. In his first report he castigated lumbermen who were "not merely stealing trees, but whole forests." The forests, he warned, would not renew themselves because of the cut-and-get-out tactics of the timber barons. He recommended the establishment of a system of federal forest reserves, the initiation of reforestation practices, charges to the users of national resources, and stiff penalties for the willful setting of forest fires.

The response to such heresy from timber-state legislators was predictably contemptuous. Speaker James G. Blaine of Maine said the Schurz program was outrageous and un-American; it would introduce "Prussian methods" into a democratic country and oppress honest enterprisers who were the backbone of the republic. To retaliate, Blaine and his colleagues chopped off Schurz's paltry appropriation for timber inspectors and the forests continued unwatched and unmanaged. But not for long. Drawing fresh support from the newly organized American Forestry Association, Schurz limped along with a limited program of reform.

Yet Schurz had shown the way. Acting belatedly on one of his recommendations, Congress authorized President Harrison to make withdrawals from the public domain and establish forest reserves. All told, Harrison set aside 13 million acres. Grover Cleveland set aside 21 million more. Then came Theodore Roosevelt, a conservationist of unequaled determination. During his stormy presidency he brought to 132 million acres the total set aside in forest reserves, a staggering and unnecessary amount as far as some members of Congress were concerned. One, Senator Henry M. Teller of Colorado, asserted that forests were being created in places where no trees grew. "I venture to say," snorted Teller, "that a two-horse team could cart off every stick of timber that ever grew or will grow on hundreds and hundreds of acres."

A second blow to the timber barons was the establishment

of the Forest Service by Gifford Pinchot in 1905. Founded with prestige, pride and an esprit de corps, the Forest Service gradually turned the American people—and subsequently some timber men—away from flagrant waste of resources to programs of wise stewardship. Pinchot himself believed that forests could be saved and used simultaneously. In his 1907 reference book for forest rangers, a slender pamphlet called *The Use of the National Forests,* Pinchot explained:

The main thing is that the land, as well as what grows on it, must be used for the purpose for which it is most valuable. On it may be built stores, hotels, residences, power plants, mills and many other things. All these are advantages to National Forests, because they help to get the fullest use out of land and its resources. Railroads, wagon roads, trails, canals, flumes, reservoirs, and telephone and power lines may be constructed whenever and wherever they are needed, as long as they do no unnecessary damage to the Forest. Improvements of this kind help to open up the country, and that is what is wanted.

Recreation in Pinchot's time was an afterthought. He summed it up in one paragraph.

Quite incidentally, also, the National Forests serve a good purpose as playgrounds for the people. They are used more or less every year by campers, hunters, fishermen, and thousands of pleasure seekers from nearby towns. They are great recreation grounds for a large part of the people of the West, and their value in this respect is well worth considering.

Once launched by Pinchot, the forestry movement quickly gathered momentum. In 1911, eastern congressmen approved the Weeks Act, and the government began to buy back cutover tracts from Maine to Florida for inclusion in a national forest system for the East. The principles taught by Pinchot and his men began to penetrate the lumber industry and some began to wonder if sustained yield was not worth a try and whether tree farming on private lands might not solve the problem of where the next crop of trees was coming from. The timber industry toyed with these ideas for several decades, subdued but not submissive to any kind of governmental regulation on their own lands. Corporations were formed, grew, diversified and began to formulate a hardnosed approach to forestry. The forestry schools supplied well-trained men whose job it was to assure a steady supply of timber from private land, a corporate mandate issued with slight regard to the balance of nature.

But one forester held the balance of nature in high regard. He was Aldo Leopold. As a professor at the University of Wisconsin, Leopold taught the interdependence of all living things and maintained that "the last word in ignorance is the man who says of a plant or animal, 'what good is it?' "

In 1924, Leopold secured protection for a large chunk of wilderness in the Gila National Forest of New Mexico. The following year Leopold wrote an eloquent plea in *American Forests* magazine for preservation of the largest wilderness tracts in the country. One result of this far-sighted forester's efforts was a system of national forest primitive areas in 1929. Under this system, certain areas of the forests were designated "primitive" and left unroaded and "unimproved"—a virtual wilderness except for one catch. There was no legislative protection for the primitive areas and the land may be taken at any time by the Forest Service and turned over to the loggers and a system of roads built over them. In the East, congressional enthusiasm for skyline drives resulted in an invasion of autos over what was formerly "primitive" land.

By 1933, it had become obvious that the principle of sustained yield was not going to work. This basic concept of forestry consists of matching cut with growth, and the match is achieved by what is called "rotation" or the length of time it takes to grow a tree to maturity. If, for example, a Douglas fir forest were on a hundred-year rotation, sustained yield would require that 1/100th of the forest be cut each year and the same 1/100th be replanted. In this way, by the end of the hundred years, the first crop planted a century before would again be ready for cutting. Thus, the forest *could* keep producing trees indefinitely, with water, soil and other factors taken into consideration. But long rotations were—and remain —unacceptable to the timber industry, which says it can grow a "mature" tree in as little as forty years, as opposed to a hundred. The problem degenerated into semantics—just what is a "mature" tree? Industry defines it not as one which has grown all it is going to grow or one which has the best quality but simply one which has sufficient board feet in it to warrant chopping it down.

With the passage of the Multiple Use-Sustained Yield Act of 1960, the forest lands were reduced to a something-for-everyone level—mine, log, ski, hunt, ride a motorbike, graze cattle, snowmobile, pitch a tent. Such use is called "balanced" by the Forest Service but clearly the true balance remains to be seen. Theoretically, the overriding purposes of the Multiple Use Act were two-fold: first, to achieve and maintain in perpetuity a high-level or regular periodic output of timber and other renewable resources of the national forests without impairment of the productivity of the land, and second, to assure that all of the basic national forest resources would be given equal consideration.

Things have not worked out that way. Roger P. Hansen, executive director of the Rocky Mountain Center on Environment, laments: "Unfortunately the concept of 'multiple use,' which should broaden the implications of public land use, has served only to narrow it again to grazing, mining, timber harvest and other consumptive uses. But multiple use cannot simply mean the grazing of sheep, cattle and horses or the harvesting of spruce, fir and pine. Nor was multiple use intended to mean all uses on every acre all of the time."

Still, the Multiple Use Act did establish some maximum control over special interest groups, which were further thwarted by what may well be the greatest conservation victory of this century: the Wilderness Act of 1964. After twenty-three different bills, eighteen emotion-packed field hearings, and seven years of bitter debate, Congress became poetic: "A wilderness . . . is an area where the earth and its community of life are untrammeled by man, where man himself is a visitor who does not remain."

Out of the smoke and fury of controversy emerged a national wilderness system that began by protecting 9.1 million acres of wild, roadless area in thirteen states. Before the end of 1974 the president and Congress must consider classifying other wilderness candidates: 5.4 million acres of national forest "primitive areas" and 50 million acres of national parks, wild-life refuges and game ranges. Since that historic day in September, 1964, when President Johnson stepped into the White House rose garden and signed the Wilderness Act, only 1 million acres (beyond the original 9.1 million) have been added, a far cry from the 50-million-acre system envisioned by wilderness proponents. Federal agencies charged with implementing the act—the Forest Service, National Park Service and Bureau of Sport Fisheries and Wildlife—have been slow in submitting recommendations. Often these agencies have been held back by vigorous opposition from commodity user groups—mining, timber and grazing.

Congress passed the Wilderness Act for several reasons. First, it did not want an exploding population—already placing our national parks in peril—to "occupy and modify all areas within the United States and its possessions, leaving no lands designated for preservation . . . in their natural condition." Second, Congress wanted to guarantee to present and future generations of Americans "the benefits of an enduring resource of wilderness."

The Wilderness Act spells out what kind of land qualifies for protection as wilderness: land of "primeval character," without "permanent improvements or human habitation"; land *primarily* affected by "the forces of nature" and with "outstanding opportunities for solitude"; land which may, and usually does, contain outstanding ecological, geological and scientific, educational, scenic or historical values.

Despite such high-minded ideals, there are certain grim realities in the Wilderness Act. Mining claims will continue to be filed in wilderness areas until December, 1983. Prospecting can proceed indefinitely, if carried on in a manner "compatible" with wilderness environment. Livestock grazing, where established prior to the Wilderness Act, likewise proceeds, apparently forever, subject to reasonable regulations. Further, the act specifically empowers the president to authorize reservoirs, power dams, roads and "other facilities needed in the public interest" if he finds that such development "will better serve the interests of the United States . . . than will its denial."

Thus even in wilderness the door is open to the commodity harvesters. And as Colorado Congressman Wayne N. Aspinall, powerful Democratic chairman of the House Committee on Interior and Insular Affairs which reviews all wilderness legislation, put it: "As to the future of the wilderness system, I think this depends entirely on the size that you have in mind . . . I do think that the wilderness concept can be carried to the extreme."

Ironically, it was Wayne Aspinall who shaped and directed the preparation of a government document which could have far-reaching effects on the availability of land that might be protected under the Wilderness Act. That document, *The Public Land Law Review Commission Report,* could literally change the face of the nation; it is the most massive review of public land policy ever assembled. Basically it recommends that multiple use give way to dominant use. Under such a policy millions of acres would be given over to the primary use of timber, millions to the primary use of mining, millions to the primary use of grazing, all with no regard to the fragile ecosystems within any given "dominant use" area.

The PLLRC report was presented to the president of the United States in June, 1970. It took three years to write, cost $7 million, weighs two pounds and lists 137 major recommendations on what to do with 755 million public-domain acres on one-third of the nation's land. Although the nineteen-member commission referred to itself as "bipartisan," twelve of its members were from western states and its chairman was the seventy-four-year-old Aspinall, longtime friend of timber, mining and grazing interests. His congressional philosophy has been that the greatest good for the greatest number is to get all we can from the public land, a view shared by most of his constituency. Thus does the PLLRC report have an overall tone of economics over aesthetics, profit over preservation, resource development over recreation. The first three pages of the report give a clue to its intent: the word "use" appears thirty-five times. The 342-page document is heavily laced with other euphemisms: "resource management," "resource development," "dominant use," "greatest net public benefit," "improvement," and "manage," a word which Webster defines as "manipulate" and "make docile or submissive to control." Nonetheless, Aspinall insisted that the commission's constant concern had been to balance commercial uses of public land with recreational and environmental objectives and that this accommodation was constructive. After all, said Aspinall, "Nature is one of the worst offenders in regard to maintaining environment."

The commission's recommendations generally call for sweeping reforms to remedy what one official called "the chaotic jungle" of more than 5,000 land laws going back to 1792. The commission itself asserts in the preface: "The probability is that upon adoption of this Commission's recommendations, no public land law will be left intact."

Some predict that no public land will be left intact either, in spite of what even the most "hysterical preservationists" agree are some excellent recommendations. Yet, overall, three major points of the report tend to favor development and inevitable disintegration of the public lands:

(1) *That Congress reassert its constitutional primacy in supervising the public lands and curb the president's power to shift public land from one use to another.*

Environmentalists fear that Congress, besieged by special interest group influence, would ultimately dispose of the public lands to those groups. Instead, they urge a new federal agency, a kind of "environmental NASA" which would "marshal scientific and technological expertise, backed by the kind of political and financial support that insured the success of the American space effort."

(2) *That land become available to states for urban expansion.*

The trouble with this is that statewide zoning exists in only one state (Hawaii) and that state and local standards for development fall far short of even passable environmental planning. Such a plan would allow the state of California, for instance, with its urban expansion grant in hand, to decide that the greatest net public benefit might be a new city containing

4 million trailers, 90 billion tons of asphalt, and 11,000 miles of neon.

(3) *That the public land laws be revised to help such commercial activities as mining, the timber industry and agriculture.*

The most appalling recommendation toward this end is the one which states, "Mineral exploration and development should have a preference over *some* or *all* other uses in much of our public lands."

It is feared that such overemphasis on mining could strip away huge sections of forest land, more even than that lost to clearcutting and overgrazing together. Congressman Aspinall's obsession with minerals was clearly demonstrated by his handling of the Wilderness Act of 1964. For two years the bill was hogtied and butchered in his committee. Aspinall finally got his way and inserted a clause that allows mining claims to be staked in wilderness areas until 1984.

The timber recommendations in the PLLRC report urged that "timber production be the dominant use" on 45 million acres of the national forests. To achieve that end, restrictions would be put on grazing and recreation. As if that were not enough, the commission lamented that "legislation creating national parks and wilderness areas . . . has reduced the area of public land—and the value of timber available from it—that is necessary to support the timber industry." To assure even greater assistance to the timber industry, the commission suggested that a federal timber corporation be set up, apparently to turn the forests into bigger and better tree factories.

Perhaps the real reason the PLLRC report pointed to the year 2000 as the "limit of its foreseeable future" is that most of the public lands may be sold off by then or may be decimated to the point where they are no longer useful—to a deer browsing or a man camping or a bird nesting or a river trying to run its course. Beneath the gloss of the PLLRC report, the dangers are spelled out, albeit inadvertently, by the commission itself. There are a number of points to consider, points pungently made by Thomas L. Kimball, executive director of the National Wildlife Federation. If the commission's recommendations were transformed into law, here is what Kimball believes would happen (and we quote):

(1) Our public lands would be managed for maximum efficiency.

Warning: The profit motive would always take precedence over public land uses that do not happen to produce jobs, personal income, or revenue for the U.S. Treasury.

(2) The proven value of "multiple use" doctrine of resource management would be replaced by a "dominant use" concept.

Warning: Public land values such as . . . the protection of unique ecological systems . . . would be allowed only if they did not conflict with mineral exploration and extraction, commercial timbering or livestock grazing operations.

(3) Public land would be sold to private individuals.

Warning: Though this particular recommendation has been cleverly camouflaged with generalities, if it became law, it would permit the sale of most of our national grasslands.

(4) The decision-making authority for public land and resource management would be taken away from the career professionals and handed to the politicians.

Warning: This could mean management by political edict. And conservationists have won very few battles in Congress against commercial interests.

(5) Everyone who uses public lands would be required to pay a fee to the U.S. Treasury.

Warning: Hunters and fishermen could be required to purchase up to four federal permits in addition to a state license. And anyone using federal land for rock hounding, hiking or bird watching would be required to pay. By contrast, mineral prospectors would not have to pay anything, at least for the first license.

(6) Major provisions of the archaic 1872 mining law, which permits mineral prospectors to freely explore most public lands unhampered by reasonable controls, would remain intact.

Warning: Miners would not have to pay reasonable fees based on the true value of extracted minerals. The Commission recommended that fees be "rather modest" and predicted that they "will not be a major source of revenue."

(7) Public land forage policies would be "flexible, designed to obtain maximum economic efficiency and to support regional economic growth."

Warning: This forage can be considered for use by wildlife and for other public purposes only after it has been used for livestock grazing ...

(8) Major timber management decisions, including allowable cut determinations, would include "specific consideration of economic factors."

Warning: Translated, this means that when demand is high, more timber could be cut, regardless of sustained yield, watershed protection, soil erosion, and outdoor recreational considerations ... Many of the Commission's recommendations sound as if they had been written by the commercial timber barons of the 19th century.

Kimball was not the only one to express fear and disgust with the PLLRC report. Citing the report's "obsession with economic factors," Hamilton Pyles of the Natural Resources

Council of America rapped the commission's concept of "maximum economic efficiency," which is "in direct contradiction to the language of the multiple use acts." Pyles called the report's recommendations "unreasonable." And *The New York Times* in an editorial of June 25, 1970, said:

> Luckily for this country the end-product of five years work by the Public Land Law Review Commission is a report, not yet a piece of legislation . . . As a study, curiously outmoded in tone, it can be read, pondered, and put on the shelf. As an omnibus bill for the reform of American land policy, it would call for alarm signals from every conservation group in the land . . . Threaded through this study is the outworn notion that the public lands should be administered, not just with economy, but with maximum economic efficiency . . . a philosophy appropriate to banking but not to the administering of nearly one-third of the country's land . . .

In February, 1971, the Sierra Club proposed four legislative steps to counteract the adverse effects of the PLLRC report. They were:

• Establishment of a National Land Reserve to include all lands already managed by the Bureau of Land Management (BLM) and repeal of all existing land disposal laws such as the Homestead Act.

• Legislation to provide a new basic act for the BLM to administer all public lands.

• Establishment of limited land-disposal procedures leading to "general public benefit" as opposed to "private economic advantage."

• Establishment of a National Forest Restoration Act to improve forestry practice on public and private lands.

Such an act, already introduced by Sen. Lee Metcalf (D.-Montana) and Rep. John Dingell (D.-Michigan) would improve forestry practices on public and private lands in the following ways:

• Require that commercial timber harvesting on privately owned lands be conducted by qualified and licensed professional foresters in accordance with forestry plans that give paramount weight to protecting the future productivity of the land, and to sustained yield,

• Provide incentives to private landowners and industry to encourage proper reforestation and adequately long rotations in harvesting,

• Direct the secretary of agriculture to conduct timber harvesting on the national forests in a fashion that accords priority to protection of the natural features and future productivity of the land, and

• Protect de facto wilderness in the national forest lands by requiring mandatory review under the Wilderness Act of 1964.

Whether this bill can get by Wayne Aspinall is debatable. In the past, Aspinall's environmental record has been a sorry one. He chopped the Senate-approved Redwood National Park bill from 64,000 acres to a minipark of 28,000 acres. Fiery debates, bad press, and attacks from his own committee members forced Aspinall to compromise and approve the present inadequate 58,000-acre park. He dealt a deathblow to the first and generous Wild Rivers Act, introduced in 1966, then came up with his own version two years later. Aspinall's bill designated only four rivers as "wild."

The attitudes reflected in the PLLRC report and by such politicians as Aspinall are not unique. Consider, for example, the thoughts of one William W. Porter II, an independent geologist writing in the January 1970 issue of *American Forests*. Among his maxims (and we quote):

Human well-being, and sometimes even survival, requires that some ecologies be exterminated, not conserved.

So-called developers are not users. They are merely agents purveying resources to the real users, the people and their government.

The land in wilderness, multiple use, recreational, and other withdrawals should be restored *now* to jurisdiction of the mining and leasing laws.

So far as mining is concerned, you don't need a wilderness act to be assured of plenty of wilderness. If land is just let alone, available to all, the mineral deposits eventually will be found, and the huge residue automatically will be wilderness.

Wilderness littered with the artifacts of a greedy civilization. A chain saw. A drill. A bulldozer. A dynamite cap. A rubber tire. A million miles of fence. And everywhere, a sea of rotting stumps.

3

We are not exploiters of a resource, we are harvesters of a resource at the behest of public demand.

—James R. Turnbull, executive vice-president,
American Plywood Association

Certainly, we have a "self-interest" in the set aside of any area containing commercial timber. Congress has said, by legislation, that we must provide the material for 26 million homes for the underprivileged in the next decade . . . We must have an expanded source of raw material—trees, in our case.

—Walter W. Black, manager,
Custer Lumber Co., Custer, S.D.

The company will step up the harvest of timber from its own forest lands and begin to maximize profits by treating the land as current profit centers rather than resource banks for future use.

—International Paper Company, annual meeting, 1968

There is recognition of the probability that whatever happens on the National Forests may well happen to private lands. Forest industries are facing widening pressures . . . agitation against tree harvesting . . . against the use of herbicides, pesticides and fertilizers.

—Dean Sherman's Forest Industry Affairs letter,
May 28, 1970

If you want to know what is ailing the lumber industry today, you have only to look at what the Government policies were yesterday. Instead of investigating the lumber industry, the administration should be investigating itself.

—Rep. James A. McClure, (R.-Idaho), March, 1971

3. The Tree Farmers

The timber industry today is a chip off the old block. A big chip—its minimum daily requirement is 100 million board feet of timber, or enough in the course of a year to form a raft of logs, lashed side by side, a mile in width, stretching all the way from New York to Lisbon. Industry operations are spread across 65 million acres, an area equal to New Hampshire, Maine, Vermont, New York and Connecticut. Industry believes it has a right to do with this land as it pleases, a right which should not be questioned by the public or by the government. The right is there because the trees are there to be cut down and made into *things*. That the forests are an endangered resource appears to matter little. If the resource runs out, there is always more, if not in this country, then in nations willing to sacrifice their forests for American dollars: the Philippines, Malaysia, Colombia, Brazil. America's leading timber company, Weyerhaeuser, presently owns or has harvest rights on more than 10 million acres in foreign countries, compared to the 5.6 million acres it owns in the United States.

On much of the acreage presently in private ownership,

there is a way of growing trees that is strikingly like growing corn or beans or wheat. Industry calls it "tree farming." Because so much of the timber resource *has* been squandered, and because industry has vastly overcut its own lands, there is a great effort these days to promote the tree farm concept. The way it works, as Sierra Club forestry consultant Gordon Robinson explains it, is simple:

"Trade associations, representing forest industries throughout the country, approach private timber landowners with a proposal to dedicate their lands as tree farms. Owners are asked to sign a statement pledging to follow three basic rules: (1) Keep tree-farm land in condition to produce timber crops; (2) protect the trees from fire, disease, insects and other damage; and (3) harvest tree-farm timber in such a way that the land will continue to produce timber for future use. What this tree-farm pledge really means is that the owner agrees not to divert his forest land to other uses after logging.

"Shortly thereafter, the proud owner is invited to a dedication ceremony at which a sign is put up in some beautiful place along a road, dignitaries are invited, speeches are made, photographs are taken. Then industry publishes annual statements showing the number of tree farms in the United States, the number of acres in the tree-farm scheme, and charts showing the curve going encouragingly upward. But here is the reality: the owner makes no pledge to match cut with growth. Sustained yield forestry consists of maintaining a fully stocked stand of trees of varied ages, and limiting cut to the quantity that grows during the cutting intervals. In tree farming, mention of this principle is carefully avoided. Yet the publicity attending the farms very cleverly insinuates that the lands are being scientifically managed for continuous production at an even rate."

Using intensified forestry on its own tree farms, industry is, in fact, able to squeeze out more lumber by one means or another. With intense cultivation methods, Weyerhaeuser has upped its volume by 33 percent. International Paper, Potlatch Forests, and St. Regis use fertilizers and genetically improved "supertrees" to get 50 to 60 percent more wood per acre. So much for the scientific and economic reasons for tree farms. Aesthetically, they are eyesores. They look like wheat fields planted with some gargantuan stock, all in long straight rows, the same distance apart, the same species, the same height, the same shape. All imperfect trees have been removed and the "forest" that has been created is sometimes fertilized, sprayed for insects and disease, and regularly thinned. There is an artificial monotonous look about a tree farm—a wildlife desert, a recreational absurdity. Yet the timber companies claim that these are "the forests of the future" and predict a similar fate for the national forests. Last year, more than one million industry-owned acres in the South and Northwest went into tree farms; the Forest Service so far has resisted the tree-farm approach, mainly because it lacks the money and manpower to implement it.

There are alternatives to tree farms. These include recycling of paper, use of substitute materials, halting exports (more on this later), and perhaps most importantly, reducing the amount of waste left in the forests after logging. Among timber men, however, the subject of recycling and waste reduction is usually dismissed with the nineteenth century logic that it costs too much, that there are still lots of forests left before they have to resort to *that*.

The Yearbook of Agriculture recently estimated that nearly one-quarter of the volume of all timber felled is wasted (later to be burned or buried). Various timber experts have estimated that proper forest practices on the poorly managed small tracts that comprise 50 percent of our national timberlands could increase their production by a factor of *five*. Nearly all of the volume now left on the forest floor could be used. Portable chippers, for example, could be used to grind slash into a residue suitable for a wide range of wood products. According to a Wilderness Society estimate, such innovations would increase the national timber supply by 10 percent.

At the sawmill, bark, which accounts for about 10 percent of the log, is burned or sold as mulch. Yet most timber men admit that it could be converted into bark board. Sawdust, which accounts for about 7 percent of the log, could be halved in volume with the use of thinner saw blades. But it would cost money to replace the old ones—a cost, said one sawmill operator, which his company was not willing to absorb. So waste is assured as long as profits are up, costs are stable, stockholders are happy, and there is no real pressure for change.

The pressure, however, is mounting. Even so, industry resists any suggestion that there might be something wrong with the way forests are being run. For every proof that waste and damage are occurring in the forests, industry produces its own expert who swears that just the opposite is true. For every justification to protect what wilderness is left, industry counters with as many arguments on why wilderness should be leveled. For those earnestly desiring to become informed, industry provides dozens of brochures, slide shows, tours of tree farms, and an army of articulate foresters and public relations men. Yet industry will not, in general, disclose any information that might reflect on how or where it has gone wrong. When asked directly the crucial question of how much virgin timber remains on Georgia-Pacific land, William J. Moshofsky, assistant to the chairman, replied:

Actually the term "virgin timber" is misleading. I assume you mean the most recent crop not harvested by man, as distinguished from the crops which have grown and are growing since man's harvesting began. Some of the so-called virgin timber is 80 years old, some 150 and some even older depending on species and location. Scientifically your question should actually have been "How much over-mature and dying timber does G-P have left?" In any event, as you can understand, we consider such information confidential but we do want to stress that we do have a substantial volume in areas where we have not yet had the chance to harvest such old timber in order to start new forests on a sustained growth program. At the point of over maturity nature starts her own harvest with windfalls that clog streambeds, lightning fires through the dried out tops, insects, disease and other natural harvesting techniques she practices.

So intent is the timber industry on getting its gospel across that it spends millions of dollars annually on full- and double-page ads in national magazines. Consider the one which appeared recently in *Time* magazine for the St. Regis Paper Company. The headline proclaimed: *"Oddly enough wild animals prefer man's way of running a forest."* On facing pages black bear, skunk, raccoon, moose, deer, grouse, deer mice, masked shrews, weasel, lynx and fox all happily frolicked amid the spruce, quaking aspen and fir. Drawings, not photographs, were used to depict this wildlife bliss. St. Regis, seventh largest timber producer in the nation, claimed in no uncertain terms: "Most people probably think a wild forest is teeming with life. While a harvested one is sterile and lifeless. Just the opposite is true."

Perhaps a "wild" forest is "sterile and lifeless" from a timber man's view. One does not have to be a wildlife biologist, however, to understand that forest animals somehow managed to survive for millennia before man came along to manage their sterile and lifeless habitat.

Potlatch Forests, Inc., fourth largest in the nation, placed what may well be the all-time winner in the November 7, 1969, issue of *Time*. This ad boasted that "It cost us a bundle but the Clearwater River still runs clear." But a team of student investigators from the Lewis-Clark Normal School in Lewiston, Idaho, learned that the photograph of the Clearwater River in the ad was taken fifty miles *upstream* from Potlatch's Lewiston pulp mill. In the ad, Potlatch insisted it had "demonstrated total commitment to pollution control," a commitment contradicted by the fact that evil-smelling discharges even then were dumped by Potlatch into the Clearwater. Immediately downstream from the plant the Clearwater joins the Snake River. In terms of loss of dissolved oxygen in the water, according to the Idaho State Health Department, Potlatch effluent entering the Snake River is equivalent to the sewage outflow of a human population of 300,000. (See Note.)

Pollution by the timber industry is not limited to water (or words). The industry also poisons the forests to protect the trees. Loggers have proceeded to pour pesticides over millions of acres to rid them of insects, an action the Forest Service still finds compatible. "Most of us are familiar with successful uses of DDT and other synthetic chemicals," boasts William Waters, chief of forest insect research. "In fact, there are very few forest insect pests for which no chemical control has shown at least partial success." The Forest Service and industry have promoted the use of ecologically crude insecticides in an inefficient, disruptive and polluting manner. They have virtually ignored pleas and protests. Yet despite their expressions of pride and confidence in the chemicals they use, the forests are still beset by insect "pests."

The Department of the Interior takes a different view of pesticides. In 1970, the then interior secretary, Walter Hickel, banned all uses of DDT, aldrin, dieldrin, endrin, DDD, mercurial compounds and 2, 4, 5-T on the 534 million acres of public lands managed by Department of the Interior bureaus. Hickel also put thirty-two other chemicals and classes of chemicals on a "restricted list," allowing them to be used only under careful control and limited circumstances.

The decision has had no influence whatsoever on industry's continuous use of some of these poisons. Bernard Orell, vice-president of Weyerhaeuser, cites the need to increase productivity:

> This means the applications of fertilizers, insecticides and herbicides much as we nurture children to the full flower of adulthood by use of medicines, nutrients and preventives . . . There are those who would ban all toxic materials . . . These would include DDT, endrin and other persistent pesticides . . . Toxic materials are essential to our lives . . . There has been a definite overreaction to the use of DDT and endrin . . .

Sharon Miller, director of forest management and research for Chesapeake Corporation, West Point, Virginia, commented at the Church hearings about the use of pesticides in the forest: "Coniferous tree seeds are coated with formulations containing endrin to repel rodents and theram to repel birds . . . These chemicals . . . are not intended to be fatal, but act as a deterrent . . . We are not attempting to kill the animals, but *educating* them to leave seeds alone (emphasis added)."

But in her book *Silent Spring,* Rachel Carson had this to say of endrin:

> Endrin is the most toxic of all the chlorinated hydrocarbons. Although rather closely related to dieldrin, a little twist in its molecular structure makes it fives times as poisonous. It makes the progenitor of all this group of insecticides, DDT, seem by comparison almost harmless. It is 15 times as poisonous as DDT to mammals, 30 times as poisonous to fish, and about 300 times as poisonous to

some birds . . . Endrin has killed enormous numbers of
fish, has fatally poisoned cattle that have wandered into
sprayed orchards, has poisoned wells, and has drawn a
sharp warning from at least one state health department
that its careless use is endangering human lives . . .

One could argue, if he wished, that the use of pesticides in
the forest becomes academic once the forest is no longer there.

Throughout all its trade journals, company literature, public
speeches, and press releases, industry pursues a single theme:
that the end (board feet) justifies the means (clearcutting).
Even when public attention focuses critically on industry's
clearcutting errors, industry does not flinch, as was the case at
the Church hearings in April, 1971. Here, all the big guns of
industry were assembled. R. V. Hansberger, chairman of the
board and president of Boise Cascade. F. L. Wyatt, senior vice-
president of Weyerhaeuser. James F. O'Donnell, vice-president
of American Plywood. George Craig, manager of the Western
Lumber Manufacturers. Dozens of somber, dark-suited timber
executives were flanked by dozens of somber, dark-suited public relations men. Throughout the three-day procedure, industry begged every issue, rationalized clearcutting with irrelevant
answers, and maintained an air of condescension toward the
public's concern.

Here are some examples of industry's attitude as they
emerged during the hearings:

James F. O'Donnell of the American Plywood Association
in Tacoma said cutting trees alongside streams improved fish
habitats by letting the sun *warm* the water. But biologists know
that without the protection of stream-side cover, water tem-
peratures rise as much as fourteen degrees in some places,
killing off such game fish as trout, steelhead and salmon, and
encouraging the proliferation of dace and other scrap fish which
thrive in warmer waters. Obviously, it was the latter species

to which Mr. O'Donnell referred. (As it turned out, O'Donnell devoted most of his testimony not to fish but to how clear-cutting in Michigan had supposedly benefited the nearly extinct Kirtland's warbler.)

F. Lowry Wyatt, senior vice-president of Weyerhaeuser, when asked by Senator Church whether most of the company's vast holdings are clearcut or selectively logged (only a percentage of the mature trees are taken), replied that Weyerhaeuser land is largely selectively cut. His testimony brought groans of disbelief from the packed hearing room. After conferring with aides, Wyatt reversed himself and said that Weyerhaeuser clearcuts most of its land. He then produced a twenty-one-page booklet depicting clearcut scenes and lovely regenerated forests in the Douglas fir region of the Northwest.

"Is this the way clearcut forests actually look?" asked Senator Church.

"We are the victims of history," said Wyatt, explaining that timber companies have not yet had the opportunity to make the forests look as they do in the booklet.

"In other words," asked Senator Church, "your forests don't actually look like this?"

"No," replied Mr. Wyatt, adding that he hoped they would.

Another Weyerhaeuser executive, George R. Stabler, director of forestry research, testified that clearcutting "makes it possible to prepare the land for rapid reforestation, reducing the time between forests." (Ecologists take issue with such a generality, pointing out that rapid reforestation is dependent on soil conditions, rainfall, sunlight, and the degree of slope. In some clearcut areas, regeneration from seed to successful seedling takes as long as ten years, and then only after repeated applications of seed.)

Writing in the December 1970 issue of *Forest Industries* magazine, William D. Hagenstein, executive vice-president of

*is encouraging to note that our Nation's annual timber
wth is now larger than the amount cut.*
"Forests Forever," U.S. Forest Service bulletin,
October, 1969

The public thinks we're raping the forests but really we are not.

James L. Wenban, deputy regional
forester, Missoula, Montana

dly enough wild animals prefer man's way of running a
st.

Time magazine, for the St. Regis Paper Company

We have to look at trees as a commodity, a property we need a return on. We have that responsibility toward fifty-five thousand stockholders.

Cy Scheider, chief forester, Boise Cascade,
interview, March, 1971

While it's fun to hike through the old-growth forest mile after mile, it gets to be pretty dreary if you don't have a cutover area once in a while so that you can get out into the sunshine.

...od has not given us these resources so we can merely watch
...eir ecological changes occur.

H. D. Bennett, executive vice-president,
Appalachian Hardwood Manufacturers, Inc.

Forestry has always been an environmental undertaking. Its main thrust has always been taming the wild forest for Man's use and enjoyment by managing the ecology instead of letting it run rampant as though there were no people around.

W. D. Hagenstein, executive vice-president
of the Industrial Forestry Association

Erosion in stream beds isn't important. Streams rehabilitate themselves anyway.

Dave Burwell, Rosboro Lumber Company
Springfield, Oregon

*Human well-being, and sometimes even survival, requires
that some ecologies be exterminated, not conserved.*

William W. Porter, II, independent
geologist in the January 1970 issue
of *American Forests* magazine

Preservationists are a selfish lot. Only a few are physically able or really want to have a wilderness experience. Ninety-nine percent of the people in New York City are never going to see it.

Bernard L. Orell, vice-president,
Weyerhaeuser Company
March, 1971

*The inaccessible wilderness and primitive areas are off-limits
to most laboring people. We must have access...*
        Julius Viancour, Western Council
        of Lumber and Sawmill Workers

the Industrial Forestry Association and past-president of the Society of American Foresters, cited a number of alleged bonuses that clearcutting provides:

Wildlife: In the case of wildlife, clearcutting transforms a biological desert into a favorable habitat by providing forage. You don't find many big game animals or birds under our century-old, dark, dank Douglas fir forests. Lower animals, just like the higher ones, crave and need sunshine for survival . . . Our animals know where it is and, except for seeking shelter during storms, you'll find most of them, as any hunter can tell you, in the cutover land in which we are manipulating the cover through clearcutting.

Fish: Clearcutting—it's good for fish. Insects—their food —develop best in cutover lands.

Watersheds: Still another bonus is the excellent watersheds developed by clearcutting old growth and replacing it with higher water yielding young trees.

Recreation: Housewives and youngsters of all ages . . . have concentrated their picking of our delicious wild black-berries and huckleberries in . . . clearcuts . . . Berrypicking is not only important recreationally for tens of thousands most every year, but provides many gastronomic multiple uses as well.

Appreciation of scenery: While it's fun to hike through the old-growth forest mile after mile, it gets to be pretty dreary if you don't have a cutover area once in a while so that you can get out into the sunshine. And it's almost impossible to see our wonderful mountain scenery where there are no roads or other clearings unless you get through, above, or beyond it to look back, down or across. So clearcutting opens up interesting vistas and creates another multiple use—appreciation of scenery.

Aesthetics: Having been privileged in recent years to have observed clearcutting . . . in Central Europe and Japan, I cannot agree professionally that it is either displeasing aesthetically . . . or destructive of the land . . . It is reassuring to observe on the slopes of Japan's most sacred shrine, Mt. Fujiyama, recent clearcuts which you can either walk through on your way up to the Shinto shrine on its peak or photograph with your new Japanese camera from the passing window of the 130-mile-an-hour Kodama train on the new Tokeido line.

In some cases, clearcutting has indeed had a minimal impact on the environment. Weyerhaeuser with 5.6 million acres to its name, Boise Cascade with 6.2 million and Georgia-Pacific with an amount it refuses to disclose but which is known to run into millions of acres, all have some forests or tree farms in good to excellent shape. Along the Coast Range, for instance, Boise Cascade owns 190,000 acres of which only 4,000 are virgin old-growth forest. In one area which receives seventy inches of rain per year, regeneration of a large clearcut logged between 1925 and 1930 has resulted in heavy stands of Douglas fir and the story is much the same throughout this particular region. Yet on some of its holdings in Idaho, Washington and Oregon, Boise Cascade has stripped the land, logged watersheds, caused soil disturbance, and had difficulty in getting the trees to grow back.

In the Umpqua National Forest in southwest Oregon, Cavitt Creek rushes through the forest, pounding over rocks, forming pools here and there where the cutthroat and brook trout like to lie. Yet just a few miles downstream from this idyllic scene, U.S. Plywood-Champion Papers has logged off some 700 acres of its own land on either side of the creek. Although it left a "leave strip" a few feet wide on either bank supposedly to protect the spawning fish, a U.S. Forest Service expert reported that the summer after the logging "the fish just fried." To complete its devastation of the Umpqua, U.S. Plywood has logged off an area of the BLM and Forest Service land above Canton Creek. The cut is about three miles long and a quarter-mile wide.

One strident Pacific Northwest conservationist claims that "all timber companies are s.o.b.'s but Weyerhaeuser is the best of the s.o.b.'s." An old, respected, family-owned firm, Weyerhaeuser nonetheless makes mistakes, too. One is along the shore of a reservoir near Gifford Pinchot National Forest in Washington where loggers have cut along the edge of the water and down steep embankments. On the recently logged eighty-acre clearcut, the ground cover was scraped away, cables and slash covered the ground, skid marks punctured the slopes and one part of the embankment had completely given way and plunged 300 feet straight down into the reservoir. The reservoir was ringed with logs from the cutting operation. And along the Olympic Peninsula where it has holdings on the south side, Weyerhaeuser has logged down to the edge of the sea, the rivers and the estuaries.

Best of the s.o.b.'s or not, Weyerhaeuser has done its share of damage to watersheds, as dramatically illustrated by N. B. Gardner, a Washington logger who wrote the following letter to the Sierra Club:

This letter is to request your help in bringing to the public's attention what is happening to our rivers and streams here in Southwest Washington, the prime offender being the big "W," or Weyerhaeuser Company. I am speaking of the rape of the watersheds of the Toutles, the Kalama, Green River, the Coweeman and their tributaries. This is occurring in big "W's" five hundred thousand-acre Mt. St. Helen's tree farm. Let me explain: I am a small tree farmer, but even I am wise enough to know that raping great areas of virgin timber along the streams' banks, filling said streams with chunks, logs, etc., is not only damaging to the ecology of the streams, but also causes drastic erosion below. Our local game protectors and biologists are helpless, due to the wealth and power of the company.

Last summer, I took on big "W" concerning the erosion of the South Toutle and North Toutle rivers. I first contacted local big "W" officials in Longview, Washington, but was met with downright hostility. I threatened to take my story to the press and television unless something drastic was done to rectify the situation, but evidently big "W" didn't take me too seriously. So on Monday, July 20, 1970, I toured the portion of the rivers as enclosed in accompanying article, with Pat Wilkins, ecology director for KATU channel 2. A.B.C., Portland, Oregon. We were also accompanied by Dick Polluck, from the Longview Daily News, Longview, Washington. On KATU's Eyewitness News at 5:30 p.m. that same evening, the film was aired as: *A logger's battle to save a river*. This showing certainly brought a great deal of embarrassment to the big "W" but has not changed their cutting practices along streams one iota.

I have just received a call from a Weyerhaeuser faller, who said to me, "I'm calling you because of the felling of the timber I am having to do along Fish Creek, a tributary of the South Toutle. My partner and I are cutting right down to the stream's edge, dumping logs, brush, tops right into the thread of the stream, and this is one of the finest Coho and Steelhead spawning streams around. No fringe area is being left alone along the creek—we are butchering it, and although I'm a faller, I'm just sick about the whole thing." He continued, "I saw you on TV last summer, and I thought you might be able to do something about it."

Fish Creek is in the big "W's" St. Helen's Tree Farm
. . . according to the faller, over a million feet of timber
has been dumped into the stream already.

Likewise, the Kalama, the Coweeman, the Green River,
etc., have all been desecrated. Management along our
banks is sorely needed.

Don't misunderstand me. Although I am a logger, I
believe in wilderness areas, but I also know that better
management practices are drastically needed in our commercial forests to save our local ecology. Also in this same
area on the South Toutle watershed there is an area of
such unbelievable beauty, called Trouble Creek, that I
personally believe that the area should never be cut, but
be preserved for perpetuity.

Please let me show somebody from your Club what
I mean. Such things as a drift of huge logs, chunks,
stumps . . . have come down from big "W's" tree farm in
only the last two freshets. Debris that goes downstream
to the Columbia, then to the sea, to plug our estuaries, and
even occasionally cause a fatality when some unsuspect-
ing person is crushed to death by one of the floating drift-
wood logs.

Any help will be appreciated concerning Fish Creek
and other debris plugged streams.

—N. B. Gardner

"To hell with the streams," said Dave Burwell, a veteran
forester with twenty years experience with Rosboro Lumber
Company of Springfield, Oregon. "Erosion in stream beds isn't
important," he said in an interview. "Streams rehabilitate
themselves anyway." With a red knit cap pulled down over his
head, Burwell stepped out of his pickup parked on a dirt road
near Impossible Creek, not far from the Willamette National
Forest in southwestern Oregon. The Willamette produces 622

million board feet of timber per year, more than any other national forest. Because of extensive clearcuts, erosion, watershed damage, and an eye-popping road system, it is probably also in the worst shape.

"That was a clearcut," Burwell said proudly, pointing to a steep slope he logged off in 1952-53 and which is now coming back with even stands of Douglas fir. He continued:

I wiped out the creek for two miles but the fish only lived and spawned in the lower quarter-mile. So the fish fry when we clearcut. They'll come back in five years. They only live five years in the first place. So we don't destroy. We only interrupt the fish life. We say okay, fish, you can't live here for five years. So we only destroy one crop of fish—they're expendable. To get out that crop of trees, it's justifiable to eliminate one crop of fish. That makes sense, doesn't it? The slopes are the important thing. If you take care of your slopes you don't get erosion in the production area. An hour after I quit logging, the stream will run clear. Well, sure I log right down to the creek bed and up the other side. I clear out the entire drainage just the way nature does with a fire. In five years you'll have your cover of alder, then the hemlock and cedar will come in and that creek will be just fine.

Clearcutting is the only way to do it. I don't care if it's eight hundred acres. The Forest Service runs scared. They take only a little piece at a time and have thirty years of disturbance. I'm a professional forester and I look for ways to prove to these guys they're wrong saying you can't log drainages, you can't make these big cuts, you have to lay out a road like it was a superhighway. When I lay out a road I don't measure it. I know it has to go from here to here. But the Forest Service is great on statistics. They measure everything. And they don't even know how many miles of roads they have on this land.

Look, I know about ecology. I know for a fact that when we clearcut we limit floods better than nature does. I know it took nature five hundred years to grow that forest and we can do it in fifty because in this climate the damn stuff grows back faster than we can cut it. I know you can log straight down the draw because that's where it's solid rock and you can't hurt it anyway. If we don't take those trees nature will. There were two thousand forest fires in Oregon last year. Two thousand! Is that good ecology to let that much timber go up in smoke?

Listen, baby, when timber is worth fifty dollars a thousand and the taxes are hitting you, you aren't going to worry about anything but getting that timber out.

Rosboro Lumber Company is small by timber company standards. It cuts 20 million board feet per year on 22,000 acres of its own land, logs another 60 million from other sources, including the national forests. Weyerhaeuser, by comparison, logs 1.8 billion board feet a year.

So fish are expendable. And the logging of watersheds is therefore justifiable. All in all, this line of reasoning is fairly consistent with industry's policy of logging what and where it pleases, whether it be its own vast lands or the national forests. But some things, one would assume, would be sacred, even to the timber industry. One would not think industry would come right out and say it wants to log off wilderness and the national parks. But it can and does say such things. What follows is the result of a series of interviews with timber executives who are convinced of the wisdom of such action.

Douglas Smith of the Western Wood Products Association: "Our argument is that an area of—let's say five thousand acres, virgin timber and without roads—has already been designated as a timber production area. It's commercial forest land by Forest Service definition and they're the managers of that land. The conservationists say that since this area is road-less it should be wilderness. The timber industry argues that Congress has passed no legislation spelling this out. We see no reason, therefore, why this area should not be managed on the multiple-use basis. This de facto wilderness situation com-promises the timber base of the nation."

Cy Scheider, chief forester, Boise Cascade: He referred to national parks, wilderness areas, primitive areas, and wildlife refuges as "areas set aside to look at or play games in." On the possibility of logging Olympic National Park: "Is it that critical to preserve a forest of big trees like spruce and hem-lock and fir? Is it so unique compared to redwood and giant sequoias? We've got bark beetles on the lodgepole pine in Yellowstone. Do we log it or let the beetles get them?"

George Hess, manager of resource programs for Weyer-haeuser: "There are great stands of Douglas fir in the Olympic National Park. Increased pressure for more wood could lead to public pressure to harvest within the park. An alternative would be to manage private and public forests as efficiently as possible to produce more wood there, so that the demand for wood does not become so great that we are forced into any set-aside area such as wilderness or national parks."

The subject of timber demand is a curious one. In 1969, when the price of lumber suddenly jumped 30 percent and plywood nearly 80 percent, Congress held three separate hear-ings to discuss not how to decrease demand, but how to squeeze more timber out of the public forests. Congress would have done well to examine the alleged 1968-69 "timber famine" more closely.

At the time of the "famine," industry demanded that the Forest Service increase the allowable cut on public lands by 10 percent. It made no move to increase cutting on its own lands for the simple reason that government timber could be had for less money—a huge saving on road building and reforestation costs which industry does not pay for on public land. At the same time, too, industry purchased 26.6 billion board feet of national forest timber which it did not immediately cut, a backlog equal to twice the annual cut. Clearly, industry was going to let it stand there until prices soared. Said Bert Cole, a former sawmill operator, now public land commissioner of the state of Washington: "It's beginning to look like someone here is pulling our leg."

Another oddity was the business of exports to Japan—2.23 billion board feet of prime Pacific Northwest logs in 1968, 35 percent more than was exported in 1967, ten times what was exported in 1960.

The strange thing about the intensity of exports in 1968 was that it was done at the expense of business at home. All along the west coast harbors, huge piles of prime saw logs awaited shipment to Japan at the same time nearby sawmills closed up for lack of supply. Yet Japan, it is known, suffered no timber shortage at this time. Indeed, the glut of the Japanese market was so great during this period that they shipped plywood, made from American wood, back to this country to keep some lumber companies here in business.

This deliberate manipulation of the market suggests gross mismanagement of the U.S. timber supply. Existing laws do not prevent American forests from being stripped or American sawmills from going out of business to keep Japan from depleting *its* forests or closing down *its* sawmills.

The manufactured crisis of 1968 and 1969 was prelude to a drive by the timber industry to lock up most of the national forest lands for intensive silviculture and logging. Faced with a shortage of raw material, industry trundled out an ingenious proposal, introduced in Congress as the "National Timber

Supply Bill." A short analysis of the legislation, then still pending, was presented in *The New Republic* by Michael McCloskey, a lawyer and executive director of the Sierra Club:

The bill seizes on the goals of the Housing Act of 1968 as a pretext for arguing that the nation needs a vast increase in lumber production if 26 million new housing units are to be built in the next decade. Under this premise, the bill then narrows its focus to argue that the national forests should supply most of this timber, despite the fact that only 19 percent of the country's forests are under federal ownership. Its ingenious argument: if intensive agricultural techniques are applied to these federal lands, growth rates of new forests can be drastically accelerated. Relying then upon accelerated growth, old forests can be quickly cleared out. To overcome the problem of paying for such intensive techniques as pruning, fertilization, and hybrid stocking, the federal government will be asked to pay all costs. The price of the timber to the industry, however, will not reflect these costs, but only the lower prices the market can carry in competition with substitutes.

To brighten the aura of this scheme, the bill was renamed "The National Forest Timber Conservation Act." It requires that intensive management be applied to all forest lands that are capable of producing marketable timber and that are not now withdrawn for recreational purposes. It sets up a high-yield timber fund into which all receipts from current national forest timber sales will be put. (These funds now go into the federal treasury to be reappropriated for many other public programs.) Finally, the bill forces the Forest Service to jump the rate of cutting immediately, in anticipation of later success in growing new timber faster (a speculative prospect).

The sudden solicitude that the timber industry is showing for the ill-housed urban ghetto dweller is transparent. The industry really wants to promote markets for its products. There *is* no timber shortage: four billion board feet are being exported in 1969 and the rate has been doubling in recent years. Housing goals can be met without any increase in timber production. Industry's real worry is that wood will be displaced in building multi-family units in city cores by lower-priced aluminum and other substitutes. It is trying to hang onto these markets by getting a plentiful enough timber supply to keep the price competitive.

Bipartisan opposition to the timber bill was led zestfully by two well-known conservation leaders in the House, John D. Dingell (D.—Mich.) and John P. Saylor (R.—Penna.). Saylor assailed the measure with an allusion to the legendary GI hamburger: he said it offered "one rabbit for the people and one horse for the timber industry." At one point, Senator Edmund S. Muskie of Maine accused the Nixon Administration of ignoring its own Environmental Policy Act. This act, signed by President Nixon on January 1, 1970, requires all federal agencies, when recommending legislation that affects the quality of the environment, to submit a detailed statement on "the environmental impact of the proposed legislation." The statement is to be sent to the president and the Council on Environmental Quality and is to be made public. Muskie charged that in the case of the Timber Supply Bill neither Agricultural Secretary Hardin nor Housing Secretary Romney had complied with this requirement. Muskie asked whether the studies called for had in fact been made. Although both secretaries had endorsed the bill, neither had submitted a statement on the environmental effect of the legislation, and neither was available for comment following Muskie's charge.

Hardin's executive assistant, E. F. Behrens (former lobbyist
for a timber industry trade association), simply said that the
bill reaffirmed the multiple-use concept and had "no environmental effect."

Ten conservation groups began mailing out literature in
opposition to the bill. Such diverse groups as the National
Wildlife Federation, the Sierra Club and the National Rifle
Association came together for a common cause: to prevent a
crass raid on the national forests.

The timber industry, meanwhile, was amassing its own
forces. One step was to align itself with the housing industry,
traditionally hostile to timber interests because of the high
prices charged for wood. This time, however, timber convinced
housing that prices would come down if increased supplies
from the national forests became available. Thus fortified with
troop strength, industry quickly inserted the word "conservation" in the bill which originally had been called the National
Forest Timber Supply Act. Next came the matter of "image."
The onerous words "Products Industry" were removed from
the name of industry's major front group, the American Forests Products Industry Association. It became "The American
Forest Institute." Thus baptized, this public relations arm of
industry sent out reams of soft-sell literature aimed at con-
vincing the public and Congress that it simply had to have
more timber from the national forests for the sake of the
nation's well-being. A brochure issued by the National Forest
Products Association, yet another voice for industry, said that
"precisely the point of H.R. 12025 was to tip the balance of
multiple use toward increased timber production."

As pressure from both sides began to mount during February, 1970, and as the House stalled in taking action with H.R.
12025, two things became apparent. One was that the sacro-
sanct principle of multiple use was obviously in danger despite

protests to the contrary by industry, congressmen and bureaucrats. The other was that the bill actually empowered Congress to *change the classification of 97 million acres of public forest,* making it in effect one gigantic tree farm. No Congress had ever attempted to decide the fate of so large an area of public domain. Typical of growing congressional doubt was the sentiment of the chairman of the House Agriculture Committee, Congressman W. R. Poage of Texas, who had said on February 6: "Frankly, I'm going to vote against it, as I see the bill now. I think it opens the door to destroy multiple use."

On February 26, 1970, the House, by a roll call of 228 to 150, refused to consider H.R. 12025. It did not vote down the bill but simply refused to bring it to the floor for debate.

Unfortunately, the victory for conservationists was short-lived.

Four months after the timber supply plan was laid to rest, President Nixon dug it up again. He directed the secretaries of Agriculture and Interior to "formulate plans to improve the level and quality of management of forest lands under their jurisdiction in order to permit increased harvest of softwood timber consistent with sustained yield, environmental quality, and multiple-use objectives." The president said that "such plans should take cognizance of the increased requirements for timber to meet our housing goals."

What did the presidential order really mean? In a bitter, yet illuminating, letter to his colleagues, Congressman Saylor wrote on June 23, 1970:

> It is with an extremely heavy heart that I inform you that the Timber Supply Act of 1970 (H.R. 12025) which the Congress rejected on February 26th recently became "law."
>
> Impossible, you say? Not at all.
>
> The Cabinet Committee on Economic Policy (upper

house?) and the Task Force on Softwood Lumber and Plywood (lower house?) recommended a disastrous, anti-public, course of action with regard to timber cutting on our public lands. During a press conference on June 19th, the President accepted the recommendations of his invisible legislators and "directed" the affected agencies of the Federal Government to carry out the policy thus established.

The effect of President Nixon's "directions" to the Agriculture, Housing and Interior Secretaries was to do by executive fiat what could not be done legislatively.

The president's order remains no more than a piece of paper, awaiting congressional funding, which does not appear forthcoming at the moment. In the meantime, the timber forces are at work again on a new bill. Introduced by timber-oriented Senator Mark Hatfield (R.-Ore.) and a number of cosponsors, the bill is called the American Forestry Act of 1971 (S. 350). It is based on the Timber Supply Act with a few new provisions to make it less obviously a blatant raid. The word "environment," for example, occurs more than a dozen times in the bill. Yet critics regard S. 350 as environmentally weak because of its vague guidelines as to what constitutes sound forest management techniques. Hailed by the timber industry, Hatfield's bill would channel logging fees back to the Forest Service via a trust fund. Reforestation would have first priority, with improvement of quality of timber management and development of other aspects of multiple use in second and third place. The bill would also provide matching grants to stimulate development of forests on private and state-owned land. All of this is aimed at more timber production on more land—the very core of the Timber Supply Act—to turn the public forests into vast tree farms.

While agreeing with such provisions of S. 350 as reforestation, conservationists lean toward S. 1734, "The Forest Lands Restoration and Protection Act," introduced by Senator Lee Metcalf of Montana. This bill is identical to H.R. 7383 which Rep. John Dingell of Michigan introduced into the House. Both bills emphasize environmental protection on any land, public or private, where logging is to be done. They specify the type of terrain on which timber cutting can take place and strictly regulate timber management practices such as clearcutting. Other environmental provisions include protection of rare and endangered species, restrictions on timber exports and protection of de facto wilderness areas until they are reviewed by Congress. Predictably, at hearings held in Atlanta and Syracuse in late summer of 1971, industry representatives were totally opposed to S. 1734.

While the congressional battles rage, other timber-related issues keep popping up in Washington, such as just how much lumber does the public actually buy when it purchases a good old 2 x 4?

A confidential congressional memo, submitted by the staff of a House investigating committee to Chairman John Dingell in the winter of 1971, warned that home-building prices may soar as a result of the new federal standards for softwood lumber. These standards spell out how much wood should actually go into lumber which is sold according to size.

The standards adopted on September 1, 1970, were "so inept and ill conceived," charged the memo, "that home builders and building supply companies held off until December and January to place orders for wood cut under the new standards." The standards created a flood of orders impossible to fill and forced softwood lumber prices to go up about 50 percent. The memo called for government action "to assure that the lumber industry does not . . . use a temporary shortage of product as an excuse to engage in excessive price gouging."

The staff memo also alleged that the new standards reduced minimum sizes and, in some cases, lumber quality. Under the new standards, a "two-by-four," previously less than 2 by 4 inches, is now actually 1½ inches by 3½ inches, or 25 percent smaller than the original. What this means is that instead of using a thousand "genuine" 2 x 4's in a house, for instance, a builder must now use 1,250 to achieve the same volume. The customer would naturally be charged up to 25 percent *more* than under the old standards.

Lumber lobbyists in the past have argued that these size reductions would result in lower lumber prices. Instead, the new leaner lumber still sells for the old fat prices.

"Rather than protecting and promoting the consumer interest by promulgating these new lumber standards," the memo concluded, "the Department of Commerce has foisted on the American public a cruel hoax that will result in less house for the money. The only gainer is the lumber manufacturer, and his gain is the consumers' loss."

That there has been an erosion of public confidence in the timber industry is beyond question. Fortunately, some timber men are beginning to realize that the time has come for change. In a recent issue of *American Forests,* whose board of directors is heavily laced with the big guns of industry, editor James B. Craig dared to write:

It seems increasingly clear we are immersed in a welter of meaningless professional cliches while at least some of our forest managers follow the lines of least resistance in our forests . . . The time has come for a very firm hand on the public forest management throttle and the hand is likely to be that of the Congress of the United States . . . We can't go on like this . . .

Amen.

4.

Right now the Forest Service is cutting about twice as much softwood as it is growing. This situation cannot last . . .

—Dr. Edward C. Crafts,
former assistant chief forester,
U.S. Forest Service,
before the Subcommittee on Forests of the
House Committee on Agriculture,
May 23, 1969

It is encouraging to note that our Nation's annual timber growth is now larger than the amount cut.

—"Forests Forever,"
U.S. Forest Service bulletin,
October, 1969

Our timber management practices and policies are based upon sound management policies backed up by sound research findings.

—Edward P. Cliff,
before a Senate Appropriations hearing,
March, 1970

The Forest Service realizes that the National Forest Management program is presently out of balance.

—U.S. Forest Service Report,
September, 1970

4. Multiple Abuse

The Forest Service wears many hats and speaks in many tongues.

Here is the career forester behind his desk in a shiny office building. He speaks of upping the allowable cut in his region while killing a wilderness proposal, of building 120 miles of timber access roads and 1 mile of trail. He says that logging the national forests is a business—like any other. *What are you going to do, let the whole thing rot?* Yet here is another who admits privately that industry has made a mess of the forests with the blessing of the Forest Service. He says his hands are tied because the last time he vetoed a proposed timber sale, the "timber boys" protested to Washington and got the decision reversed. *If I reduce the allowable cut, know what will happen? They'll move me out of this national forest and put me where I can't make decisions.*

Away from their offices, their reports, their 100-page timber sale contracts, most of the men of the U.S. Forest Service are ardent woodsmen, the sensitive-to-nature kind of rangers that Gifford Pinchot recruited at the turn of the century—at least at the lower echelons. They love the service and take pride in it. And yet, among an increasing number of foresters, there is dissatisfaction with the way the service is run, fear that it has lost sight of its goals, bitterness about the influence of the timber industry, and a fervent wish for reform.

Few men in the Forest Service feel free to speak out. Their reluctance to do so is best explained by G. M. Brandborg of Hamilton, Montana, a veteran of forty years with the Forest Service (beginning as a laborer and advancing to supervisor of the Bitterroot National Forest before his retirement in 1955). A craggy-faced, raw-boned man with a shock of snow-white hair, "Brandy," as everyone calls him, wrote in "The Blue Ribbon Commission" report on timber management in the national forests:

> The Hatch Act has often been used as the crutch to keep men in public service from speaking out on issues, and from taking leadership in conservation for which their training, knowledge, experience, and position qualified them . . . From personal experience I can tell you that such a public servant who will speak out when the time comes to speak out is not looked upon with favor by those in position of power over him. Many able administrators are cast into limbo because they are men with conscience and a sense of duty.

One sad journey into limbo was that of Harold Wadley, former district ranger for the Shoshone National Forest at Dubois, Wyoming. Upon his arrival there in 1968, Wadley took one look at the devastation of Wyoming's high country and immediately put a stop order on some imminent sales. He scaled down others where he could. Later, the courageous ranger announced to a stunned audience (largely made up of lumber people) that not only had he reduced the allowable cut from 17 million board feet in 1968 to 3.8 million for 1969, but that a new timber survey would probably push it down even further. Late in 1969 Wadley submitted his timber management plan with the allowable cut drastically reduced. He expressed confidence that it would be accepted by early 1970. It wasn't. The months dragged on while top-echelon Forest Service bureaucrats came to Dubois to check and double-check on Wadley and his plan. Finally, almost one year later, word came through that the new plan had been approved by Chief Cliff and the Forest Service hierarchy. The price for the plan was Wadley's transfer. He was notified that he had been put in charge of a Job Corps Camp at Chadron, Nebraska, far from the forest he knows and loves so well.

On rare occasions the Forest Service does stand up to industry. One such occasion was the appearance in 1968 of Arthur W. Greeley, Jr., associate chief of the Forest Service, before a meeting of the Western Wood Products Association in Colorado Springs, Colorado, at a time when supporters of the Timber Supply Act were mustering strength. Greeley took industry to task for a so-called "Problems Paper" it had submitted to the Forest Service. The paper complained about everything from tighter air and water pollution controls to the lack of a favorable public image. Some of Greeley's points:

On air pollution: State enactments now made and to be made will lead to complications in your lives . . . I think it is clear that air pollution considerations may well come to be dominant in many future decisions on how we manage timber and how you harvest it.

On water pollution: My concern is about soil moving into streams as a result of road building and logging. We have not seen anything yet compared to what we will be seeing—problems of policing to deal with stream water quality, with silt in the streams, with treatment of side streams . . . In your Problems Paper you are objecting to things we ask for now in the area of erosion control and watershed protection. It is my flat prediction that our requirements are not tight enough now . . . and that we are going to have to go further with more restrictions than is the case now.

On multiple use: You want timber put first in the multiple use priorities . . . I have to conclude from your Problems Paper that there are segments of the forest industry that think multiple use is all right as long as timber is the beneficiary, but who are not really ready to accept or make concessions about other users who have an entirely proper desire to make use of public properties . . . The Paper says that Forest Service philosophy tends to "restrict realization of the raw material potential of the commercial forests lands." And again, that we are reducing the supply of economically available timber by "special and costly harvesting requirements to meet aesthetic objectives." The Paper charges us with abandoning timber management in some areas in order to promote "preservation of scenery," and charges that we "fear" pressure from recreationists. It points out what is classed as "needless" threatening of our commercial forest land base. It urges that "timber management must be stressed as the dominant use which enhances other uses . . ."

We feel we have an obligation and directive from Congress and from the people to manage the national forests for multiple use. You feel somehow that timber activities are being discriminated against, are not being given their appropriate place in the sun, and are being asked to move aside . . . to accommodate some of these other public uses of public land.

On erosion: We have differences of opinion on how to treat unstable soil areas. It's an oversimplification to say we "fear" erosion. Erosion problems are very real . . . I don't see how we can disregard soil stability needs . . .

On a quarter-million-acre addition to the Bob Marshall Wilderness: We've opposed this suggested addition to this wilderness and we are still in opposition. The supporters of this wilderness proposal oppose the methods of logging and road construction that have been used—especially one road. Literally we teeter on the edge of a decision *against* commercial timber operation in this area because the public will not accept what the Forest Service and forest industry have dished out as being good enough logging practice.

On improving their image: I'm convinced the public thinks we've given them the back of our hands—the forest industry and the Forest Service . . . We can't establish a favorable image primarily by magazine ads and the paternal beneficence of Smokey Bear.

Alas, Greeley's straight-talk failed to straighten out the industry. Not long after the associate chief's commendable speech, industry proceeded to promote the Timber Supply Act —with the ultimate blessing of the chief of the Forest Service.

Perhaps it is the Forest Service which should be straightened out first. Tangled in functionalism, keyed to commodity production rather than environmental protection, manipulated by the timber industry and challenged by the public, the service is on the defensive for the first time in its sixty-six years. Its direction is unclear. It seems wholly unresponsive to public needs— possibly because it is unable to determine *what* the public needs really are. Thus, hand in hand with the timber industry, the service plods along. Chief Cliff gave some indication of why the service falters when he presented his side of the story at the second session of the Church hearings on May 7, 1971. Responding to the accusation that the Forest Service had violated the Multiple Use and Sustained Yield Act of 1960, Chief Cliff replied: "Multiple use means different things to different people . . . Multiple Use is defined by the act in a broad way. The act does not tell us what the appropriate balance is between national forest resource uses."

Exactly. In fact, this benighted branch of the Department of Agriculture is saddled with one of the more difficult and idealistic mandates ever handed a public agency in the United States. The landmark act commands the Forest Service to balance equitably the use of its lands among "outdoor recreation, range timber, watershed and wildlife and fish purposes." Sustained yield was intended to provide for the development of the various forest resources, including timber, but only at a level that would never result in the resources being used up, mined or turned over to grazing.

Chapter 2140 of the Forest Service Manual, which deals with multiple-use surveys, reflects the lack of direction as it begins: "Multiple use surveys are impact surveys . . ." This does not fit the context of an act that talks of multiple use as the "harmonious and coordinated management of the various resources, each with the other, without impairment to the productivity of the land . . ." *Impact,* indeed. In Chapter 2130, which deals with Ranger District Multiple Use plans, the manual says that management decisions for development policy must be "nonfunctional," a word Webster defines as "not serving a useful purpose."

Aside from the confusing semantics of forestry, the service is further compromised by its own timber sale practices. Unlike proposed wilderness additions, which require hearings before any acreage can be set aside, notice of a timber sale is sent to the lumber companies and ads are placed in the small local weeklies of the logging communities. No effort is made to contact conservation groups who might wish to protest or at least have a voice in deciding what is to be logged. Timber contracts are awarded on a bid basis.

Although bidding is supposed to be competitive and open, sales often are so tailored to the needs of a particular local mill that it is almost certain to get the contract. In addition, buyers of national forest timber frequently agree among themselves in advance of bidding to keep prices under control. Homer Hixon, deputy chief in charge of timber management in the Forest Service headquarters in Washington, D.C., admits that "there may be a few cases of collusion in bidding. We've suspected it a few times and we're sensitive to it. But it's very hard to prove." He could not recall a lumber buyer ever being convicted for engaging in collusive bidding.

In Oregon, one sawmill operator says there is an unwritten agreement among certain mills and lumber companies as to who will bid on *what* and *where*. Everyone sticks to the bargain, he says, and everyone gets a piece of the action. Some bid only on thinning sales, others only on large sales, still others are only interested in salvaging what the Douglas fir saw-log operators don't want.

"If I bid on a sale I'm not supposed to, or raise a ruckus about running them logs there through the creek and up the hill," says the man from Oregon, "you can bet that at the next sale I'm supposed to get, one of the big boys will be there and outbid me."

Richard Schloemer, an ex-Forest Service employee and former forester for the Conner Lumber Company of Victor, Montana, has seen a timber sale from both sides. Schloemer says:

Timber sales are laid out for certain mills. The type of timber a mill needs, be it of large or small diameter, is always available. My concern rose when I realized that if the mills wanted to increase their capacity, the timber just happened to increase its growth at the same rate. On the Bitterroot National Forest, the Intermountain Lumber Company increased its capacity from 130,000 board feet of lumber per day to 200,000. The Conner Lumber Company went from 75,000 to 200,000 board feet per day in a two-year period. During the same period, the Van Evans Company of Missoula began to bid on sales in the Bitterroot and obtained 12 to 15 million board feet of timber per year. When I came to the Bitterroot five years ago, the annual cut was around 40 million board feet a year. By 1970, the Forest Service had sold 70 million board feet and the annual cut is now claimed to be 58 million board feet per year. True, as the Forest Service claims, some of this is different type timber and of a smaller class than before. However, after having looked at every sale and having hiked over 90 percent of the Bitterroot, my personal observation leads me to believe that the increase is due to pressure group tactics and a lack of understanding by the Forest Service, rather than in a form of better timber management.

After the timber contract is let, the next step is the construction of logging roads. The cost of these roads is high. The average road in the Bitterroot National Forest, for example, ranges from $50,000 to $150,000 per mile. The service engineers the roads, the lumber company builds them. The lumber company also receives the full construction costs as credit. After the Forest Service deducts its own costs of administering the sale and the engineering of the roads, there is not enough left for reforestation.

After the roads are in, the loggers start to cut. The good logs are marked, bucked (cut into manageable sections) and hauled out the easiest way—by tractor, or by a cable system which usually just drags the logs along the ground to a landing, the place where big diesel equipment lifts the logs onto waiting trucks which then speed them to the mill. When the logging is finished, a bulldozer comes along and shoves the left-overs into giant slash piles for burning. As much as 50 percent of a stand may go up in smoke, and the Forest Service is left with a charred, scarred hillside—where reforestation is supposed to take place, where the forest animals are supposed to browse, and where recreationists are supposed to camp.

A case in point is the Fish Creek drainage in Wyoming's Teton National Forest, once one of the West's finest elk habitats. The creek starts just below the Continental Divide, cuts through long open ridges, lush meadows, big parks and wide valleys. In 1967, the area was logged. Now a first-class gravel road penetrates the area, leading directly to the huge U.S. Plywood mill in Dubois. Logging roads push into every large stand of trees. About half of the trees in the drainage have been taken, mostly from clearcuts of up to eighty acres in size. The logged land is scarred and eroded, and there is scant sign of reforestation. During the spring, heavy rains added to the melting snow from the Divide turn Fish Creek and other streams in this drainage into rivers of mud. The fish are gone from Fish Creek now. The elk population of 2,000 has been cut in half and is expected to drop even lower. In summer, the creek sometimes dries up and wind blows silt from the creek bed up the banks and it settles lightly on the stumps.

This, says the Forest Service, is Multiple Use.

The regeneration of Wyoming's fragile subalpine slopes (7,500 to 10,000 feet) is slow. From Shoshone National Forest come reports that some 16,000 acres in that district have failed to regenerate after 30 years. Noting that in such a severe climate it takes between 135 and 300 years for a new forest to reach maturity, Senator Gale McGee concluded bitterly:

"In this country, when you talk about harvesting timber, you are really talking about wiping out a forest."

Though U.S. Plywood's throbbing diesel armada annually removes some 50 million board feet of timber from Wyoming's high country, Wyoming's real future lies with recreation. Fifty miles west of the sawmills at Dubois, the national forests abut the region's two great national parks: Yellowstone and Grand Teton. In the summer of 1970, nearly five million visitors descended on these parks. More than two million visited the three national forests (Shoshone, Teton and Bridger). Growing numbers of backpackers and trail riders are surging into Wyoming's wilderness despite efforts by timber interests to keep them out.

Significantly, in 1970 no funds were allocated for campground construction in Wyoming's national forests, even though overcrowding was even then beginning to decimate the landscape. In Teton National Forest, Supervisor Bob Safran views the recreation incursion as a threat and says his forest is becoming "a bedroom for the national parks." Seventy miles south, Bridger Forest rangers have been trying to move a large boy scout camp from the shores of a clear lake to a dead-water pond full of leeches. Throughout the national forests, officials grumble about "the hippies" invading their domain, about campground litter and the costs of repairing everything from privies to picnic tables. Yet no one grumbles about the massive effort—and expense—required to clean up after the loggers pass through.

Between the loggers' mess and burned-over land (from lightning fires), some 5 million acres in the national forests are in need of reforestation. Moreover, the Forest Service acknowledges that an additional 13 million acres of commercial forest land need timber-stand improvements of one kind or another. The price tag for all this is estimated to be $900 million. Yet the Forest Service has budgeted only $27 million for reforestation in fiscal 1972—a drop in the bucket compared to the more than $100 million budgeted for timber sales and the construction of timber access roads.

At its present rate of replanting only 230,000 acres a year, it will take the Forest Service until 1992 to catch up with its reforestation goals. And while the cutting continues, the Forest Service boasts: "It is encouraging to note that our Nation's annual timber growth is now larger than the amount cut." Such a statement stretches the facts—unless one includes all of the timber on private land as well as the Forest Service's lands: 187 million acres (including wilderness, and not just the 97 million designated as "commercial forest").

The service defines commercial forest land as that which is capable of producing twenty-five cubic feet of wood per acre per year. It is a definition as mythical as "multiple use." Millions of acres in the subalpine regions of Wyoming, Montana and Idaho do not contain this volume. Still, they are logged. The Whiskey Creek drainage containing virgin ponderosa pine in Wyoming's Medicine Bow National Forest, for example, is capable of producing only about fourteen cubic feet per acre per year. Yet the Forest Service wants to log this 25,000-acre forest. Conservationists want to add it to the wilderness system. The Forest Service's last word was that Wyoming had more than its share of wilderness already. (Although it has *none* which contain samples of big ponderosa pine.)

In the administration of the forest reserves it must be clearly borne in mind that all land is to be devoted to its most productive use for the permanent good of the whole people and not for the temporary benefit of individuals or companies.

—Gifford Pinchot,
first chief, U.S. Forest Service, 1905

5. Emasculating
the Wilderness

For many years the philosophy of Gifford Pinchot permeated the Forest Service. And the service grew strong and earned respect because it had faith in the people and justified the faith the people had in it. Prior to World War II, the service was a healthy, viable institution. It appeared to be a practitioner of good stewardship and, up to then, to be running its own course with little interference from industry. As Pinchot wrote: "No generation can be allowed needlessly to damage or reduce future general wealth and welfare by the way it uses or misuses any natural resources." The Forest Service believed it was so. Characteristically, it refused to compromise the land base of the nation. Typical of its stance in the late thirties was the reaction of Ferdinand A. Silcox, then chief of the Forest Service, to a rather curious proposition.

Silcox was asked to advise on the soundness of a government loan for enlarging a western lumbermill which was cutting 50 million board feet a year. The mill wanted to triple its production and sought to borrow $3,500,000. It figured to pay off the loan in eight years, provide badly needed jobs at the mill, and increase its own profits. This seemed practical, and in tune with the system of free enterprise—so the mill waited confidently for Silcox's reply. When it came, the answer was no. He explained it with the philosophy of the early forestry movement, oriented to public welfare and social reform. He pointed out that after the loan had been paid, the timber cut, and the investors satisfied, the town would be sunk and the government would have to pay the relief bill, just as it had done already in mill town after mill town across the country.

In Silcox's day, the forestry schools were likely to turn out a breed of idealists determined to halt the wholesale destruction of the forests by the timber barons and to rescue the decimated range from the cattlemen. But after World War II, the emphasis was on how to get the most out of every acre, a new approach which sacrificed land ethics for land economics. And along with this new approach came a new acceptance of clearcutting.

Douglas fir, as it happened, was discovered to reproduce poorly in some places under the partial cover left by selective cutting. So industry began to accelerate its liquidation of west coast fir forests. Instead of cutting small patches or narrow strips to permit seeding from the forest edge, as well-trained silviculturists had been doing for years, loggers spread out from the small openings surrounded by large timber to whole valleys and vast mountainsides. For the most part, the Forest Service was careful to keep the devastation from public view. Along the major highways of the Northwest, forests and streams and mountainsides, generally, still look like picture post cards. Yet on the other side of the mountain, the devastation often runs from ridge to ridge.

During the 1960s the timber establishment expanded its

clearcutting procedures to include any forest with a stand of merchantable timber on it—the ancient, slow-growing hardwoods of the East, the slower growing ponderosa and subalpine fir of the Rockies. New machines were introduced; new foresters were there to keep prodding for better and better production (but not for better and better protection), and the Forest Service itself fell into playing a role of resource manipulator. The new forester, armed with a computer and a concept of economic efficiency, invented something called "high yield forestry," which increased allowable cut by shortening rotations and rationalized clearcutting as being necessary for the mass production of timber. And still the Forest Service continued to speak of multiple use.

Congressional funding of the Forest Service during the last eight years illustrates graphically the gap between intent and performance (see chart). Apparently, no lesson from this imbalance of budgeting allocations—95 percent of full financing for timber management, only 52 percent for soil and water management—has been absorbed either by the administration or the Public Land Law Review Commission. The Public Land Law Review Commission report, the so-called National Timber Supply Bill, and a bill authored by Senator Hatfield of Oregon under the misnomer "American Forestry Act of 1971," all emphasize designation of "dominant timber production units" and provide for special funding for timber management. The PLLRC proposed a "Federal Timber Corporation," the Timber Supply Bill an earmarked fund, and Senator Hatfield a "Forestland Management Fund"—all exclusively dedicated to timber production. In fact, at the hearings on the two bills before Congress in Portland, Oregon, August 9, 1971, Senator Hatfield declared he would not be satisfied with any timber legislation that did not authorize increased sale of timber from the national forests.

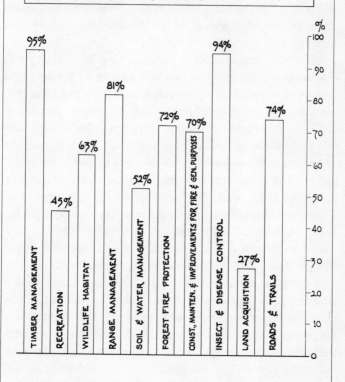

THE BUDGET GAP

THE CHART HERE ILLUSTRATES THE LEVEL OF FUNDING GRANTED BY CONGRESS FOR FOREST SERVICE PROGRAMS. FOR EXAMPLE, 95 PERCENT OF THE FUNDS REQUESTED FOR TIMBER MANAGEMENT WERE AUTHORIZED; FOR SOIL AND WATER MANAGEMENT, ONLY 52 PERCENT. DATA IS BASED ON FIGURES COMPILED BY CHARLES H. STODDARD, VICE CHAIRMAN OF THE NATIONAL COMMITTEE FOR BETTER FORESTRY.

Program	%
TIMBER MANAGEMENT	95%
RECREATION	45%
WILDLIFE HABITAT	63%
RANGE MANAGEMENT	81%
SOIL & WATER MANAGEMENT	52%
FOREST FIRE PROTECTION	72%
CONST., MAINTEN. & IMPROVEMENTS FOR FIRE & GEN. PURPOSES	70%
INSECT & DISEASE CONTROL	94%
LAND ACQUISITION	27%
ROADS & TRAILS	74%

The emphasis on production inevitably precludes any real government effort at protection. It is clear, for example, that the Forest Service is basically unsure of its commitment to wilderness preservation. Top officials deny this vehemently, pointing out that the service established the first wilderness and primitive areas back in the thirties. But what they don't say is that over the years the service has continually reduced the sizes of these preserved areas to let the loggers in. This precipitated the move by conservationists for the Wilderness Act, which removes the fate of wilderness from administrative whim and places it in the hands of Congress. The Forest Service has resented this infringement on its bureaucratic powers ever since.

The 1964 act immediately set aside as wilderness 9.1 million acres and allotted ten years to add more acreage by a process of agency hearings, nominations by the president, and congressional enactment. But where wilderness proponents envisioned that some 40 million acres would be added during this period, the actual acreage processed for congressional approval had totaled only 1 million acres by 1971. An executive order may be shaping up in the White House to speed up this process. In effect, the order would instruct agencies to forbid development that might damage any potential wilderness area before Congress can act. However, this is now forestalled by President Nixon's recent appointment of a Forest Review Board with timber industry representatives on it.

Sometimes, wilderness proposals are emasculated by administrative fiat—especially those drafted by the Forest Service. Always, it seems, the wilderness acreage omitted from the service's proposals contains the greatest amount of merchantable timber in the virgin, old-growth stands. In some cases, the service has crushed hopes for wilderness by announcing plans for a road that would cut the area in two—as in the proposed Alpine Lakes Wilderness in Washington. Actual logging is always the major issue.

In Colorado, for example, the Forest Service in 1969 announced a timber sale on 17,000 acres of the East Meadow Creek area of the White River National Forest, under review at that time for reclassification as a wilderness area. Aroused citizens promptly filed suit against the service and Kaibab Industries, a large western logging firm, arguing that logging would preclude adding the superscenic area to the wilderness system. U.S. District Judge William E. Doyle was unimpressed by the government's plea to cut. "No more horribles, please," the judge warned Regional Forester David Nordwall, after *Colorado Magazine* presented picture after picture of clearcut devastation not far from the proposed East Meadow Creek area. Then the judge asked Nordwall what he thought of such timber practices.

"This is not a very good example of proper forestry," Nordwall replied with considerable embarrassment.

The judge turned thumbs down on the defendants. The case is now under appeal by the government and the logging industry.

Elsewhere, the service's record is equally bleak:

• *Idaho:* The Forest Service apparently intends to propose logging of much of the 1.2 million-acre Idaho Primitive Area, leaving only a fraction for wilderness classification when it comes up for review. Also in Idaho is the Magruder Corridor, where the loggers have been held off by conservationists for nearly thirty years. This 250,000-acre upper drainage of the Selway River has been under constant threat of the saw since the Forest Service declassified it from the Selway-Bitterroot Wilderness. Independent ecologists have warned that the area is too fragile to cut. The Forest Service is not impressed with their arguments.

• *Oregon:* Citizens have been fighting for years to prevent logging of French Pete, one of the last unspoiled drainages in the Cascades. No other valley in western Oregon remains with a continuous stretch of unbroken, old-growth virgin forest, unroaded and unlogged, from low elevation to timberline. In eastern Oregon, the twelve-year battle over the Minam River drainage continues to rage as conservationists struggle to add it to the Eagle Cap Wilderness Area. The Minam is the last major woodland valley left uncut in eastern Oregon. The Forest Service seems determined to permit logging there.

• *North Carolina:* The Joyce Kilmer Memorial Forest (3,800 acres set aside in 1935) contains one of the few virgin stands in the Appalachian Mountains. In 1970 the Forest Service meekly approved a U.S. highway right-of-way that will slash through the edge of the Kilmer Forest, leaving vast cuts and fills, and destroying some of the best trout streams in the East.

• *Southeast Alaska:* The Forest Service has sold off all the commercial timber on nearly 4 million acres of the breathtakingly beautiful Tongass National Forest, some 16 million acres big. Whole valleys, coves, shores, and heads of bays have been stripped or are committed to being stripped under a bizarre 50-year contract. Because the rotation period is 100 years, and one of the conditions of a contract is that the bidder must construct a pulp mill, a built-in demand is created for the rest of the virgin forest after that first 50 years. What this really means is that instead of "only 4 million acres" being ravaged, at least another 4 million are doomed under the self-perpetuation clause of the contract. All of this controversial Tongass acreage is of course the best, in terms of trees and terrain and unspoiled beauty—until the loggers move in. In addition to the big contracts awarded by the Forest Service, other smaller but just as devastating timber sales are being awarded to "independent" loggers who then sell right away to the big pulp mills which thereby have greatly expanded their capacity beyond the sales volume specified in their own contracts. The Forest Service, following a "timber first" policy, has violated the Multiple Use Act again and again in the Tongass.

The philosophy of the Forest Service toward wilderness is echoed in its attitude toward recreation. *Recreation interferes with logging,* the service often implies. *The two may not be compatible on the same piece of land.*

The Forest Service's Pacific Southwest Experiment Station in Berkeley conducted a study in 1962 to determine the maximum possible impact of recreation development on timber production in three California national forests. Researchers wanted to determine if it was even possible for recreationists to "take over" the national forests. So the study was designed to assume a maximum conflict: recreation was taken to be wholly incompatible with timber production. What would, they asked, be the maximum timber displacement—assuming all these exaggerated conditions—if recreation were fully developed on all suitable lands in the three forests?

The impact of recreation on timber management was measured in three ways: salable stumpage devoted to recreation; annual allowable cut foregone for recreation; and reduction of sustained yield capacity from recreation use. Five types of recreation sites were used in the study: occupancy sites, activity sites, unusual interest areas, wilderness areas and protective zones. Here are some of the study findings:

(1) Assuming that every single, possible suitable acre was devoted *exclusively* to one of the five types of recreation uses, only 10-12 percent of the three forests would be involved in "competition" with timber production.

(2) Investment capital for recreation development is the limiting factor, not lack of suitable land or competition

with timber production. "The problem . . . is not one of a general scarcity of suitable land . . . but rather one of an 'embarrassment of riches' that requires rational scheduling of development."

(3) The recreation capacity of the three forests studied could be increased ten times with a reduction in sustained timber yield capacity of only 13 percent. In other words, assuming maximum conflict between recreation and timber management and maximum wilderness development, it was found that the 3.5 million acres of the Modoc, Sierra and San Bernardino National Forests could provide 40 million visitor days of recreation plus 240 million board feet of timber at sustained yield capacity.

Phil Briegleb, one-time director of the Forest Service Pacific Northwest Experiment Station in Portland, Oregon, has proposed this hypothetical experiment:

Forest X has 250,000 acres now managed for sustained yield timber products. A local conservation group wants 25,000 acres to make an addition to Wilderness Area Y. The battle is joined. Timber producers, local labor unions and the chamber of commerce charge that this will reduce the annual cut by 10 percent or 10 million board feet; that workers will be thrown on relief; that timber products prices will skyrocket, in lieu of tax payments to local counties will fall off, and widows and orphans will be thrown into the streets of mournful ghost towns. But instead of wailing over the "loss" of 25,000 acres, what if a little forestry is practiced on the remaining 225,000 acres through accelerated tree planting and systematic precommercial thinning? Let's say that the cost runs as high as $225,000 annually but that the investment increases production by 10 million board feet a year with a stumpage value of $500,000 and a gross product of $8.5 million. In this case, the *increase in timber yield* obtained by better management is just equal to the loss in timber output due to the 25,000-acre withdrawal. The *net* cost to the local economy—which would be more than made up by tourism and recreation expenditures— would be $225,000 annually.

It was against a setting of bitter controversy that a special committee at the University of Montana issued a report in November, 1970, on the Bitterroot National Forest in Montana—a report hailed by conservation groups and some foresters, denounced by the timber industry, and received with mixed feelings by the Forest Service. For the list of charges leveled at the Forest Service by the Montana team was recognized as containing much of what is wrong with the service nationwide. The "Bolle Report"—named after its principal author, Arnold W. Bolle, dean of the university's School of Forestry—came up with some shattering findings:

(1) Multiple-use management, in fact, does not exist as the governing principle on the Bitterroot National Forest (BNF).

(2) Quality timber management and harvest practices are missing. Consideration of recreation, watershed, wildlife and grazing appear as afterthoughts.

(3) The management sequence of clearcutting-terracing-planting cannot be justified as an investment for producing timber on the BNF. We doubt that the BNF can continue to produce timber at the present harvest level.

(4) Clearcutting and planting are an expensive operation. Its use should bear some relationship to the capability of the site to return the cost invested.

(5) The practice of terracing on the BNF should be stopped. Existing terraced areas should be dedicated for research.

(6) A clear distinction must be made between timber management and timber mining. Timber management, i.e. continuous production of timber crops, is rational only on highly productive sites, where an appropriate rate of return on invested capital can be expected. All other timber cutting activities must be considered as timber mining.

(7) Hydrologic, habitat, and aesthetic values must be preserved by single-tree selection cutting, a minimum disturbance of all residual vegetation, and the use of a minimum-standard, one-time, temporary road.

(8) The research basis for management of the BNF is too weak to support the management practices used on the forest.

(9) Unless the job of total quality management is recognized by the agency leadership, the necessary financing for the complete task will not be aggressively sought.

(10) Manpower and budget limitations of public resource agencies do not at present allow for essential staffing and for integrated multiple-use planning.

(11) Present manpower ceilings prevent adequate staffing on the BNF. Adequate staffing requires people professionally trained and qualified through experience.

(12) The quantitative shortage of staff specialists will never be resolved unless the qualitative issue with respect to such specialists is first resolved.

(13) We find the bureaucratic line structure, as it operates, archaic, undesirable and subject to change. The manager on the ground should be much nearer the top of the career ladder.

(14) The Forest Service as an effective and efficient bureaucracy needs to be reconstructed so that substantial, responsible, local public participation in the process of

policy formation and decision making can naturally take place.

(15) It appears inconceivable and incongruous to us that at this time, with the great emphasis upon a broad multiple-use approach to our natural resources—especially those remaining in public ownership—that any representative group or institution in our society would advocate a dominant-use philosophy with respect to our natural resources. Yet it is our judgment that this is precisely what is occurring through the federal appropriation process, via executive order and the Public Land Law Review Commission's Report.

The problem (said the Bolle team) arises from public dissatisfaction with the Bitterroot National Forest's overriding concern for sawtimber production. It is compounded by an apparent insensitivity to the related forest uses and to the local public's interest in environmental values.

In a federal agency which measures success primarily by the quantity of timber produced weekly, monthly and annually, the staff of the Bitterroot National Forest finds itself unable to change its course, to give anything but token recognition to related values, or to involve most of the local public in any way but as antagonists.

The heavy timber orientation is built in by legislative action and control, by executive direction and by budgetary restriction. It is further reinforced by the agency's own hiring and promotion policies and it is rationalized in the doctrines of its professional expertise.

This rigid system developed during the expanded effort to meet national housing needs during the postwar boom. It continues to exist in the face of a considerable change in our value system—a rising public concern with environmental quality. While the national demand for timber has abated considerably, the major emphasis on timber production continues.

The postwar production boom may be justified by the single-minded emphasis on timber production. But the continued emphasis largely ignores the economics of regeneration; it ignores related forest values; it ignores local social concerns; and it is simply out of step with changes in our society since the postwar years. The needs of the postwar boom were met at considerable social as well as economic cost. While the rate and methods of cutting and regeneration can be defended on a purely technical basis, they are difficult to defend on either environmental or long-run economic grounds.

Many local people regard the timber production emphasis as an alien orientation, exploiting the local resource for nonlocal benefit. It is difficult for them to distinguish what they see from the older forest exploitation which we deplored in other regions. They feel left out of any policy formation or decision making and so resort to protest as the only available means of being heard.

Many of the employees of the Forest Service are aware of the problems and are dissatisfied with the position of the agency. They recognize the agency is in trouble, but they find it impossible to change, or, at least, to change fast enough.

Multiple use is stated as the guiding principle of the Forest Service. Given wide lip-service, it cannot be said to be operational on the Bitterroot National Forest at this time.

A change in funding to increase considerably the activities in nontimber uses would help, but could not be effective until legislative and executive emphasis changed.

But even with this modification the internal bureaucracy of the agency and the lack of public involvement in decision making make real change unlikely.

As long as short-run emphasis on timber production overrides long-run (and short-run) concern for related uses and local environmental quality, real change is impossible and the outlook is for continued conflict and discontent.

The university committee was made up of Bolle, three other forestry professors, a wildlife professor, a sociologist and a political scientist. It was established at the request of Senator Lee Metcalf (D.-Montana), who had received numerous complaints from constituents about conditions in the Bitterroot Forest.

Reaction to the Bolle report was predictable. Said Edward L. Schults, vice-president of Tree Farmers, Inc.: "The report is a political accommodation, designed to castigate and discredit and intimidate the Forest Service and to support obstructionist groups who want to stop all timber cutting in the national forests." He blamed the criticism on "people like the Sierra Club who pose as conservationists but really are damned, hardcore preservationists, who always want to tie up commercial timber land in wilderness, and take it out of the economy. We can't waste all these resources. Just for housing alone, we're far behind now on timber production."

Schults's firm is a branch of the Intermountain Company, a Missoula lumber firm which gets two-thirds of its logs from the Bitterroot Forest—or about 40 million board feet per year, out of a total of 63.3 million board feet cut altogether in the Bitterroot in 1969.

At the Forest Service regional office in Missoula, Deputy Regional Forester James L. Wenban said: "The public thinks we're raping the forests but really we are not. We are not in

bed with the timber industry." Wenban pointed out that the
Bolle report was preceded by a toughly worded Forest Service
task force appraisal of management practices on the Bitterroot
Forest.

The service task force was mobilized by Regional Forester
Neal Rahm following local outcry about what was happening
to the forest. The group was given free rein to write what it
wished without any Forest Service editing (significantly, the
six-man team was made up entirely of Forest Service personnel). The report, though it was a searching self-examination of
service practices, was cautiously worded. It failed to explain
why the ponderosa pine stands were so seriously overcut. It
also failed to pinpoint responsibility for the devastation of the
Bitterroot which caused the furor in the first place. The task
force upheld the practice of clearcutting and terracing, although
it acknowledged that clearcutting had been overdone. In response to charges about watershed damage, the task force
replied: "We have not been able to substantiate the claims of
widespread watershed damage due to logging, roadbuilding
and terracing." Although the report said that the allowable cut
for the forest was not too high, it admitted ponderosa had been
overcut because allowable cut calculations had been "misinter-
preted." Yet on the all-important question of forestry philosophy, the task force came straight to the point. "There is an
implicit attitude among many people on the staff of the Bitterroot National Forest that resource production goals come first
and that land management considerations take second place."

Task force leader William A. Worf, regional chief of recreation and lands, explained his few, strong points of disagreement
with the Bolle report: "We disagree on what they said about the
need for timber. The need for wood and wood fiber is increasing." Replied Dean Arnold Bolle: "The Forest Service always
predicts lumber shortages. The projections just do not add up.

There is no shortage now, the lumber component in housing is shifting as substitute materials are developed, there is no assurance that housing goals will be met. To some extent, the projected demand for lumber is a scare tactic."

The Bolle report, the task force report on the Bitterroot, and growing public dissatisfaction about despoliation of the American forest paved the way for the Church hearings. The sessions clearly documented the dangers of clearcutting and put the Forest Service under new pressure to change its faulty forestry.

Throughout the hearings, Chief Cliff sat almost unnoticed toward the back of the crowded, high-ceilinged room, puffing on his pipe and listening attentively as irate citizens called for the government to oust him from his post. The beleaguered Cliff also heard complaints from industry, for whose sake, said some conservationists, he had "sold out" the remaining stands of timber and stripped the land.

At the end of the third day, Senator Church, who had guided the hearings with finesse, insight, and impeccable cool, said wearily: "We do everything in the name of multiple use but we may not actually be practicing multiple use at all. There's a great deal of room for argument about the meaning of multiple use. I've heard mining interests use multiple use as justification for unrestricted mining. But show me an open-faced mine and then show me another use for the area."

Church observed that "a large piece of clearcut land has obviously usurped the other uses. Logging has become the dominant use." He suggested to the Wyoming delegation: "Maybe we need to back up from this oversimplification called multiple use in which its application is nonexistent." The Idaho lawmaker argued that in areas where the greatest use of the land is for scenery and recreation, "It makes little sense to permit logging that seriously detracts from the scenic attraction. There are other areas where more intensive logging would be more appropriate."

Highlights from the testimony reveal some disturbing facts:

• Dr. Robert Curry of the University of Montana charged that clearcutting so depletes the soils of nitrogen and other nutrients that two or three crops of timber may be all that can be expected in many areas before they are made utterly barren. Dr. Curry said it would be possible to rotate crops of trees, using nitrogen-fixing alders alternately with generations of commercial timber trees, but that a generation of timber would be lost. Although clearcutting might be feasible in the flat pine forest of the South, he testified, "it is definitely not good in the western states."

• The next blockbuster was delivered by Hurlon C. Ray of the Northwest Region Office of the Federal Water Quality Administration. He said that sediment in streams can increase from less than 10 parts per million (ppm) under natural conditions to more than 70,000 ppm in improperly logged areas. Ray said that the sediment comes primarily from dragging logs down slopes and through streams. He told the senators that the logs should be pulled uphill and that the roads should be located uphill, instead of near and through stream beds. The scientist suggested that helicopters or balloons might be used to remove logs without damage to the soils.

• Another outspoken witness, Dr. Donald H. Gray, acting director of the Institute for Environmental Quality and associate professor of civil engineering at the University of Michigan, tore into the Forest Service's road-building policies. He said that road building in clearcut areas must be held to an absolute minimum and the size of the cuts reduced. Steep watersheds should not be cut at all, he insisted, but reserved for recreation, wildlife and watershed uses. Dr. Gray testified that although clearcutting weakens slope strength, which leads to landslides, road building "may have the more serious impact."

- Gordon Robinson, the Sierra Club's forestry consultant, cited a case in which the Forest Service had oversold one Alaskan timber sale by 800 percent. "The timber was just not there," said Robinson, "but they went ahead and sold it anyway."

- Charles H. Stoddard, a forester and former director of the Bureau of Land Management and now a resource consultant, attacked Senator Mark Hatfield's "Forestry Act." Mr. Stoddard termed it "an attempt to revive the Timber Supply Act," an accusation which brought gasps from the audience and considerable irritation from Hatfield, who sits on the subcommittee.

- Donald W. Chapman, aquatic biologist for the U.S. Bureau of Sport Fisheries and Wildlife, suggested that the entire Forest Service be removed from the Department of Agriculture and placed in a new Department of Environment and Ecology. Dr. Chapman charged that only traditionally educated foresters, oriented toward timber production, can ever be in charge at the district ranger level. "At present it is all but impossible for a wildlife or fishery biologist or watershed specialist to become district ranger," he said. "We must kill the allowable-cut straight jacket, for it prostitutes the bureaucracy and makes it a single-use, not a multiple-use agency. If we do not kill the allowable cut, let us develop concomitant 'allowable harvests' of elk, deer, visitor days, grouse, trout and water."

Answering his critics at the second round of the Church hearings a month later, Chief Cliff was imperturbable and completely convinced that his forest management plan is sound. His implication was that the expert witnesses at the first round of the Church hearings were misguided, misinformed, and above all, tampering with the bureaucratic immunity of the Forest Service. The most revealing part of his testimony came when, under questioning from Senator Church about the regeneration costs exceeding the profits on the Bitterroot Forest, he replied: "If this country is going to have all the resources it needs in the future, it may *have* to subsidize the timberlands." The alarming part of this theory is that as far as Chief Cliff and the Forest Service are concerned there is nothing wrong in expecting the American people to pick up the tab for the timber tempest—roads, regeneration, and whatever mess the stump merchants have made of public land. Chief Cliff and Secretary Hardin fail to recognize that the timber industry is responsible for *all* of these woes. As in other industries, woe should be part of the cost of doing business. Who in the automotive industry, for instance, would dare suggest that the government come in and clean up its waste, build roads to bring its raw material in, or see that its source of minerals is subsidized? In recent history, only the Lockheed Aircraft Corporation has achieved this kind of public subsidy for private gain.

As for the question of depleting the nation's timber supply, Senator Church pointed out that the annual cut had zoomed from 5.6 billion board feet in 1950 to nearly 12 billion in 1969 and that there had been an 18-million-acre increase in national forest land classified as "commercial" between 1945 and 1971. Chief Cliff hesitated, then admitted that "we may have included some areas we shouldn't have."

Despite his stiff-necked attitude toward timber at the Church hearings in May, Chief Cliff displayed an entirely different philosophy at a Senate hearing on September 16, 1971. As Senator Bob Packwood of Oregon struggled to convince an intractable Subcommittee on Parks and Recreation that there ought to be a 750,000-acre Hells Canyon-Snake National River in Idaho, Oregon and Washington, Chief Cliff rose to the aid of the conservationists. He said, "It is our feeling that there should be no dams on the sixty- to eighty-mile stretch within our jurisdiction." To the chagrin of timber industry witnesses who followed him, Cliff was willing to place into wilderness all 211,000 forested acres of Packwood's proposal—Forest Service acres containing nearly two billion board feet of merchantable timber. In a brief interview following his testimony, the chief said that although he personally leans toward Packwood's bill, Forest Service policy is governed by the administration. Asked what he would do if the administration pushed for a dam instead of wilderness, the chief shook his head and said, "That's the kind of dilemma I face most of the time."

6.

Harvesting timber is like harvesting wheat—but growing timber is measured in decades instead of months. When timber is cut there is a temporary loss of beauty. There is also the promise of what is to come, a thinned new forest replacing the old. The pattern of management you see here assures that future generations of Americans will always have timber—and natural beauty.

> U. S. Forest Service sign at the entrance to the
> Cranberry Backcountry, a de facto wilderness area in
> the Monongahela National Forest of West Virginia

Asking the lumber industry if it can produce more lumber is like asking the agricultural industry if it can produce more corn.

> —Dr. John Meunch, Jr.,
> forest economist for the
> National Forest Products Association

Why damage the beans while harvesting the corn?

> —Don McClung, a Richwood, West Virginia, coal miner

6. The View East:

Monongahela

Spring comes late to the mountains of West Virginia. In early April there is only the hint of new life stirring in the forest. The sturdy old hardwoods seem to hold back the unfolding of new leaves, as if spring were a thing to be savored. In the Cranberry Backcountry, snow hugs the shaded slopes in April, covering dead leaves and the green, insistent plants struggling upward. It is at this time of year that the people of Richwood also begin to stir, harkening to the gentle mountains and to the swift, fresh streams with funny names. *Barrenshe Run. The Queer Branch. The Hell for Certain.* They come to the forest then to feel the damp earth beneath their fingers, for somewhere beneath the dead leaves and the melting snow is a delicacy known for miles around as ramps—a wild onion so pungent that the West Virginians say that if you eat one you have to hide for two days.

On one particular spring morning two old friends came to the Monongahela to hunt for ramps. They stood facing the

Forest Service sign at the edge of the Cranberry Backcountry and looked away to the Alleghenies so hazy and graceful and quiet. Howard Deitz, in a hunting cap with one flap down, with a cheekful of tobacco and his one good eye turned skyward, didn't go to work that morning. His shoe store on Richwood's Main Street would wait. The forest and the ramps were somehow more important. The same with Bob Smith, a stocky ex-Marine who owns a toy store and newsstand across the street from Deitz.

Beyond the sign offering so much hope and bureaucratic reassurance was a dead forest. Some of it lying down dead. Some of it standing up dead. Any way you looked at it, dead. Back in 1968 the Forest Service allowed loggers to clearcut this 15-acre patch. Not much, considering there is a 549-acre clearcut just over the hill at a place called Hunter's Run. Too bad about Hunter's Run. In cutting down all the trees, they also obliterated part of the Pocahontas Trail, an honest-to-goodness Indian trail that got its start about the time Columbus was hunting around for America. The Forest Service says it's sorry about that. Not that it won't allow clearcutting anymore, just that it won't allow the loggers to chop down so much all in one place. How much can they chop down? Well, says Howard Deitz, 80 percent of the Monongahela is scheduled to be clearcut sooner or later. May take them a hundred years to do it, considering the forest is 820,000 acres and the trees mature slowly.

*   *   *

Research and experience have clearly demonstrated that the evenaged management system, which includes clearcutting, is the best way to manage our forest's timber stands. We, therefore, do not intend to depart from evenaged management as the basic timber management system on the Monongahela National Forest . . . This intensive management will help to sustain the important existing timber industry as well as help to meet the certain future high demands for wood products.

Those people who would stop all timber cutting must realize that they are also dependent on wood and paper products for many of their daily needs. Those people who would convert all public lands into hunting preserves must understand that the public also needs developed recreation areas. The Forest Service is leading the way in recreation development and expansion of tourism. We are also committed to sustaining the existing economy and jobs provided by the timber industry.

Widespread selective timber cutting as advocated by the Chamber of Commerce would eventually reduce the allowable cut and endanger the future of the timber industry.   —Frederick A. Dorrell, supervisor, Monongahela National Forest

*   *   *

Howard Deitz and Bob Smith worked their way down a steep, muddy path through the clearcut. The logging of three years before had removed only those trees desirable for market —the lumberman's arbitrary choice of size and species. All else had been cut down and burned, or left to die standing up by an ingenious method called girdling. The tree is chopped with an axe all the way around and then, just to make sure it will die, is injected with a herbicide. (Girdling is performed to provide "den trees" for squirrels and birds.) A 200-year-old birch was thus killed and stood in the midst of the debris left by the clearcut—debris through which a new forest, planted in 1970, would blossom forth by 1988.

Would the new forest be composed of the superb mixed hardwoods—the ash, maple, hickory, hemlock, beech, birch and basswood—which characterize much of the Monongahela?

No. As part of what it considers good forestry, the Forest Service regenerates with a few fast-growing species requiring much sunlight. Because such trees produce timber swiftly and profitably, the Forest Service calls them "desirable" species.

"Just what is a desirable species?" asked Howard Deitz, squirting a stream of tobacco juice over a fallen tree. "How do they know that in eighty years a poplar will still be preferable to the so-called undesirable hemlock? And how can they be so sure that what's left here to rot doesn't have some remarkable value?"

*   *   *

The harvest is controlled, and special measures are taken following logging to establish and care for the new forest. . . . We plan to soften the effects of clearcutting. . . . In many of these areas the logging of decadent timber and its replacement with vigorous, young, green trees will be a contribution to esthetics itself.

We carefully control the location and grades of roads used on national forest timber sales. . . . When the harvest is completed, skid roads, temporary truck roads, and disturbed areas are closed and seeded with grasses and cover plants.   —Frederick A. Dorrell

*   *   *

Coming out of the clearcut, the two old friends passed through a narrow strip of trees left along the logging road, left there, as Frederick A. Dorrell put it, because "in accordance with multiple use management we will modify timber harvest in recreation developments, roadside zones, scenic areas, and waterside zones." A kind of camouflage, as if you could not see the ravaged forest for the trees along the road.

What *about* the road, with its so-called "carefully controlled grade," its seeding "with grass and cover plants?" For about a mile this twenty-foot-wide road, used just once during logging, has indeed been reseeded and eventually there will be a good carpet of grass. But above and below it are several other roads, as close as a hundred feet apart, running up and across the hillsides. Safely out of sight, they are not seeded with anything unless it is the indignation of men like Deitz and Smith. Where the seeding stops on the main logging road, you can see the ruts made by heavy equipment and places where numerous streams have cut across the road carrying precious topsoil and nutrients from the clearcut areas with them.

Howard Deitz shifted the tobacco from one side of his mouth to the other. "You want to know about the grade up ahead?" he asked, pointing to the side of the hill where the road climbed abruptly at the edge of yet another clearcut. "The Forest Service says only an 8 percent grade is allowed in the Monongahela but that one just happens to be between 18 and 20 percent. They say it won't happen again. Just one of those things."

The two men walked rapidly, turning away from the logging road. For a mile or so the forest was intact. Moss and vines hung from the noble hardwoods, last cut at the turn of the century and now halfway to maturity. The leafy rhododendrons nodded in the cool wind and sunlight struck the buds beginning to unfold into pale, waxy flowers. In the hushed, shadowy depths of the forest there was the chattering of birds. A squirrel poked its head through the branches of a young beech, teetered uncertainly, then scampered away. A ruffed grouse appeared in the clearing, stared solemnly at the two men, then went off into the brush. It is in this lovely undisturbed forest that men of Richwood have hunted for turkey and deer and grouse and squirrel, sometimes with a perfect pair of hounds. ("That," says Howard Deitz, "is one of the important things in life.") Near here too the men have fished the clear and sparkling Cranberry River, one of the nation's best trout streams. But the projected clearcutting on the steep slopes on either side of the river is certain to ruin the fishing.

Suddenly the magnificent forest ended as Deitz and Smith emerged into one of the Monongahela's most severe clearcuts, a ninety-five-acre tract on the drainage of a steep and rocky hillside. All of the trees had been cut down or girdled, the ground cover stripped away. Dead trees leaned at crazy angles, roots exposed, branches clawing at the sky. The land on either side of the stream was badly eroded.

*   *   *

Some of our critics have acclaimed the good job our timber sale administrators do in protecting the streams. We appreciate this but don't intend to rest on our laurels.

—Frederick A. Dorrell

*   *   *

Bob Smith's big hands slowly folded into fists. "I'm a grown man," he said, "but when I see this it makes me want to cry."

Howard Deitz didn't say anything for a while, just sat on a stump and chewed. Then he got up and walked quietly back the way he had come, stopping after a while to turn his one good eye toward an eighty-foot high maple standing alone on the top of a barren ridge. "That's my tree," he said and tipped his hunting hat to it the way he always did whenever he passed by. Then he and Smith found a place where the forest was still alive and dug in the earth for ramps.

Howard Deitz and Bob Smith are not sentimental or hysterical. Nor are they versed in theories of forest management. They happen to like trees. They happen not to like what the Forest Service is doing to them. And so they—along with most of Richwood's population of 4,000—set out to save the Monongahela a couple of years back. Not unusual perhaps for a state which calls itself West (By God) Virginia. Perhaps unusual for a coal mining town where you hear about moonshine and revenuers and are quietly reminded that there are no blacks for sixty

miles around. The Monongahela is at Richwood's backdoor
and from it has come a flow of timber. And timber was what
put the town on the map in the first place. It began at the turn
of the century when the timber boom swept across West Virginia and brought industry and prosperity—a tannery, a paper
mill, a clothespin factory, a tub and handle factory. But by
1937, the good, easily obtainable timber was virtually gone
and Richwood seemed the victim of "cut and get out." Since
saved by strip mining and tourism, Richwood no longer depends on timber. That is why it is able to wage war on the
Forest Service.

Lawrence Deitz, a wiry, bespectacled insurance man who is
Howard's first cousin, has become one of the state's most
knowledgeable laymen on the subject of timber and an outspoken foe of Forest Service timber practices in the Monongahela. As a leader of what he jokingly calls "a small band of
malcontents," Deitz aided in the creation by the West Virginia
legislature of a special "Forest Management Practices Commission." In August, 1970, the commission issued a blistering
report charging that the Forest Service practices on the Monongahela were "timber oriented" to the exclusion of other forest
uses as dictated by the Multiple Use-Sustained Yield Act of
1960.

The West Virginia commission found that the areas in which
the Forest Service had permitted clearcutting were—following
the cutting—aesthetically undesirable and unusable for recreation for ten to fifteen years. The 549-acre clearcut at Hunter's
Run had been an important habitat for wild turkeys and bear.
Both species reportedly disappeared from the run after the
clearcut. To describe this particular devastated area, U.S. Senator Jennings Randolph of West Virginia used the term "shock-
ing" and went on to say that on such a steep slope severe erosion was bound to occur. He complained that "the entire area

was covered with usable pulpwood, slash and dying timber."

The recommendation of the commission was that clearcutting be practiced on the Monongahela only in rare cases where even-aged management is the only way to achieve regrowth. In addition, the commission said, clearcut areas should be small and well dispersed and clearcutting should be limited to a fraction of a percent of the total forest land in any one year.

While the commission was taking the Forest Service to task in the summer of 1970, the Forest Service itself engaged in a bit of self-criticism. At the insistence of a by-then outraged Senator Randolph, Chief Cliff ordered another special task force report which, while confessing some grave errors on the Monongahela, essentially refused to change the clearcutting policy. Some commendable points were made in this report, however, regarding the general symptoms of a diseased service. Among them:

1. Official statements that multiple use is actively pursued when, in truth, it is underplanned and undermanned.

2. Early emphasis that all-age management was the best forest-management system followed by an abrupt change in policy to even-aged management.

3. Publishing self-commendatory brochures and annual reports of Forest Service activities that are dull or exaggerated.

4. Self-assurance that if a program is technically right, it should automatically have public acceptance.

5. Implying that management-specialists take an active part in planning and designing timber sales when in actuality they do not.

The task force report admitted that the Forest Service is indeed timber-oriented by pointing out that while there are nineteen timber managers in the Monongahela, only nine specialists are assigned to oversee water, recreation, and landscape

values. It lamented that "timber was the only single-use program that had quantitative goals, pressures to meet them, and
personnel to carry them out. Basically at fault are present
organizational and financial systems that continue to emphasize
timber management above all other resources despite multiply-
ing evidence that public demands today call for the multiple-
use the Service has better preached than practiced."

One of the Deitzes' allies is Ralph O. Smoot, a retired
professional forester who served as district ranger on the
Monongahela. His view of the Forest Service today is that
under pressure from the timber industry it has changed to the
point where "a ranger is graded on whether he meets a quota
for cutting timber." Smoot recalls that when he was with the
Forest Service the controversial Hunter's Run section was sold
and cut under his direction, using the selective cut method. He
allowed only mature hardwoods to be removed while other
younger trees were left to continue their natural growth later
on. However, eight years later, because the pressure was on,
the entire area was clearcut. In a technical sense, said Smoot, the
Forest Service is correct when it insists that clearcutting is the
best method of logging. It is quick and easy and when the cutover land grows back it produces trees of the same age and size
which can then be logged and handled with speed at the
sawmills.

"In other words," said Smoot, "it's efficient. But that doesn't
mean that's the way a national forest should be operated."

With all the reports in, the recommendations issued, and
superficial attempts made at appeasing the West Virginians by
such things as leaving the forest undisturbed along roads and
scenic areas, the Forest Service still continues to sanction clearcutting in the Monongahela. It continues to endanger wildlife
habitat and watersheds and to impair the soil, perhaps for all
time. It was only under intense questioning at a congressional

hearing that the Forest Service admitted that it had plans here for seventeen timber contracts in 4½ months, sales that were to yield nearly 50 million board feet of lumber, a quantity roughly equivalent to an entire year's cutting in the past. These contracts represented 5,281 acres of clearcutting and only 2,608 acres of selective cutting. At this rate, critics say the estimated 31,000 acres of mature timber will soon be gone.

Meanwhile, in Richwood itself is one of the most dramatic indications of just how far the Forest Service has been allowed to go. At the Georgia-Pacific sawmill, the logging trucks roll in hour after hour, carrying huge logs from the state's last virgin stand of mixed hardwoods, a 3,300-acre site now being cut on the Meadow River. It was one of these fine old logs, a 300-year-old white oak, that caught the eye of Howard and Lawrence Deitz one afternoon as they went down to the Cherry River to see what was happening at the sawmill. Lawrence bent over the huge log and spreading his fingers measured it across with his hand.

"Thirty-six inches, Howard," he said firmly.

But Howard Deitz appraised the log with his one good eye and shook his head. "I think it's forty, Lawrence."

"But I just measured it, Howard," insisted the wiry man with glasses. And then with a lumberman's rule, he found he had, in fact, erred by a quarter of an inch.

Going home just as an orange sun was sinking into the low hills, Howard lifted his head and remarked to his cousin, "Used to want to set foot on every square inch of land within a hundred-mile radius of Richwood, Lawrence. I guess I'm going to die before I do it."

Then he said, "Well, there're some parts I don't want to see anymore anyway."

7

One of my most unforgettable moments of the past years is walking through the Redwoods last November—seeing the lovely shafts of light filtering through the trees so far above, feeling the majesty and silence of that forest, and watching a salmon rise in one of those swift streams—all our problems seemed to fall into perspective and I think every one of us walked out more serene and happier.

—Lady Bird Johnson,
July 30, 1969,
words in bronze on tablet in
Redwood National Park

If you've seen one redwood, you've seen them all.

—Ronald Reagan,
governor, state of California

7. The View West:

Redwood Creek

They stand alone in their majesty, taller than any living thing, creaking and bending in the wind like old men with rheumatism. The late afternoon sun touches the crowns of these kings and spills down the coarse and ancient trunks to the floor of the forest where the smaller trees grow—the Sitka spruce, the bigleaf maple, the rhododendron and dogwood, the aggressive tan oak and the madrone with shiny green leaves and bright red limbs resembling plastic. Beneath these are five-finger ferns, pale green and delicate, striped horsetails, buttercups and huckleberries, pink trillium, yellow violets and the rare calypso lady's-slipper orchids, and the clintonia, shyly hiding its delicate clusters of tiny red flowers so small and insignificant some 350 feet beneath the canopy of *Sequoia sempervirens*—the coastal redwoods, ever-living sequoias. The light gives magic to the groves whose oldest trees were there before Christ died on the cross.

Moss-barked, solid, straight and massive, the redwoods glow

in the warm light of late afternoon, red, brown and silvery gray. They have witnessed more than half a million dawns, have felt millennia of rain, have stood there as animals and plants lived and died beneath their branches, have marked time as eighty generations of mankind came and went. And the redwoods kept living. A citadel to life, a link to a time of dinosaurs, a tribute to nature's wild nobility.

And a prime target for destruction.

In northern California, long before the plunder of the redwoods began in the 1840s, some 2,000,000 acres of those magnificent giants occupied the moist coastal region. Today only 145,000 acres of lands which once grew redwoods have been set aside in state and national parks, and of this total only 66,000 acres are virgin. In the hands of the logging companies there are less than 100,000 acres of old-growth redwoods left. At the present rate of cutting, all of this may well be gone before the end of this decade. Then the timber companies will be forced to log second-growth redwoods that at most can be no older than 130 years, one-fifteenth the age of the virgin forests that are being logged today. But a second-growth redwood is a second-rate redwood, a facsimile of the monarchs that have fallen to the chain saws.

How safe is safe? How much of the 66,000 acres of virgin redwoods in state parks and the Redwood National Park will remain in perpetuity as monuments to ages? Because not one entire watershed of significance was acquired when the parks were set aside, some scientists believe heavy upstream logging will eventually kill the "preserved" redwoods as well. Pointing to such alarming facts as the twelve tons of silt that wash down the heavily logged Eel River each year, and the 1955 flash flood that toppled more than 300 major trees and washed away 50 acres of land on the Bull Creek flats, some ecologists fear a similar fate for the national park on Redwood Creek itself.

The inadequate size of the park was determined by dollars and politics. The Sierra Club tried in vain to nail down 90,000 acres in the Redwood Creek watershed, part of a proposed 93,000-acre park which would have stretched from ridge to ridge. During the three-year battle, Georgia-Pacific and Arcata Redwood continued to log within proposed park boundaries: and today they continue to log right to the edge of the park itself. The 58,000-acre compromise-park cost the government $92 million in 1968, the most expensive park ever authorized at any time or in any place. The result is an odd-shaped park, forty-six miles long and seven miles across at its greatest width. On the map, it resembles a Rorschach blot. Aesthetically and ecologically indefensible, the park should have a 40,000-acre expansion to survive. Yet even that will not do away with the ubiquitous logging trucks crowding out the tourists on the road nor silence the chain saws and the bulldozers so loud that there is almost no place in the park where you do not hear them.

One pale spring morning when the mist was still blowing in from the Pacific, curling in and out of trees and hurrying across beaches and the mouths of rivers, Dave Van de Mark of Trinidad, California, set off in a pickup truck for Redwood Creek. When the controversy was at its height, Van de Mark photographed logging activities and used his pictures to rally conservationists. Some lumbermen say privately that Van de Mark may have risked his life.

U.S. 101 parallels the coast and runs through grove after grove of redwoods, past signs announcing Georgia-Pacific's holdings, past dozens of teepee-burner sawmills, past a scene of apocalyptic devastation near Prairie Creek Redwood State Park (where not a tree was left standing when Arcata Redwood Company logged down to the highway in 1962). Every other vehicle on this highway is a logging truck, carrying huge redwood logs and huge Douglas fir logs to the sawmills. Not surprising—considering the fact that Humboldt County produces some 1.3 million board feet per year, most of it redwood (a cut, incidentally, that exceeds annual growth by 270 percent).

Off the highway now, past a huge sawmill, its teepee-burner turning scraps into eye-stinging smoke, its yards piled high with whole forests of incredible redwood logs thirty and forty feet long, as much as sixteen feet in girth. More logging trucks, brakes shrieking, coming down the hill, on the same road used by the tourists. These roads are public and the immense logging trucks have as much right to them as any visitor, given the weird compromises that Congress made with industry to create the patchwork park. So intricate were these compromises that in certain areas of the park the federal government owns the land but the timber companies own whatever trees have fallen on it. The National Park Service is still surveying boundaries, still promising a master plan any day now and still trying to pacify the timber industry which is busily cutting a ring around the park and haggling with the administration over the price of the land it lost.

Chain saws and logging trucks, clearcuts and caterpillars. This is a first impression of Redwood National Park from the road. (Most of the park lies west of the road and is accessible only by foot.) Just outside the park, hundreds and hundreds of acres of clearcuts sweep up the slopes and down the other side. A thousand acres here. A drainage wiped out there. On the ground the fallen slash lies, rotting. And somewhere on the side of a slope near Redwood Creek they are at it again. The whine of the chain saws, like a rasping cry of some monstrous insect, echoes through the trees.

Van de Mark stops his truck and gets out. There is a rubber raft stuffed in his pack. With oars in hand, he follows an old logging road toward the rasp of the chain saw. Then off the road. The forest becomes more dense. Van de Mark pushes on.

There are red plastic ribbons fluttering from some of the red-woods. They are marked to be felled. Arcata Redwood Company is chewing up the forest on this side of Redwood Creek and Georgia-Pacific is at it on the other. The forest Van de Mark struggles through will be leveled by the end of the year. In time, the second growth will come in. Not as big or as noble or as awesome. But redwoods all the same. Commercial timber. . . . The saws are silent for a moment. Then the ripping snapping shrieking of a redwood going down.

It takes about an hour to kill a redwood. To clear away the brush, to chop holes in the side of the tree and shove in boards for a platform from which to cut, to grind into the heart of the tree with a saw. And so they work, two men to a tree, making what's called a Humboldt cut angled up to join a horizontal cut.

The forest smells of freshly cut timber and pitch, and dust from the 'cats crossing the logging road and knocking down the small trees so they can get at the big ones easier. Van de Mark is close now. He can see the sawdust spurt from a red-wood as two men with strong and steady arms patiently cut through fifty years of the tree's life in less time than it takes to fry an egg. The rasp of the saws grows louder toward the end. The sawdust sprays out into the faces of the men in the hard hats. The old redwood just stands there as if nothing were happening to it. Then the cutting stops. The men climb down from the platform. The crown of the tree trembles a little. The branches wave. The thick, mossy trunk begins to tilt. Finally, with great ripping and snapping, the oldest part of it tears loose from the stump. But there is another, more distinct sound before the great tree pounds flat against the earth. It is a cry—some men have described it as a scream—from an organism that has no voice.

On to Redwood Creek. With Van de Mark.

In May, the creek's waters are quiet and the raft drifts over the shallows, running aground now and then on sandbars. The redwoods close in. Small streams drop through dense banks of dogwoods and rhododendron. A raccoon sniffs along the water's edge. Here, too, is a merganser, a mother duck with eleven ducklings too young to fly, a great blue heron motionless as a sculpture in the shallows, a rare red-tailed hawk high on the cool wind, an osprey guarding its nest.

The quarter-mile strip of parkland on either side of Redwood Creek creates an illusion of wilderness. But this is soon shattered by the whine of a chain saw. Just beyond the quarter-mile strip is an 800-foot buffer zone, a sort of DMZ. And beyond that is the private land where redwoods are being felled. How long this fragile wall of trees along the creek will stand is anybody's guess, for their roots are shallow and they are susceptible to wind-throw.

In the gathering dusk, Van de Mark beaches his raft. He sits with his feet in the water, watching the stars come out in the corridor of sky over Redwood Creek. Against that sky, the tall trees somehow appear diminished. *How long will they last?* Van de Mark wonders, too.

*   *   *

After seeing what was happening to the redwoods, I went to Portland, Oregon, to interview a tall, soft-spoken lawyer named Bill Moshofsky, assistant to the chairman of Georgia-Pacific. In a handsome paneled office Moshofsky sat back in his chair and spoke of the battle which took so much redwood acreage from Georgia-Pacific. "There are one million seven hundred and fifty thousand redwoods in the state parks, enough to make a solid row trunk by trunk from San Francisco to New York," he said. "This is how monstrous this hoax was."

He had some opinions on other things, too.

On redwood rotations: "In a hundred years we can get a redwood six feet in diameter—if we wait that long. With the new technology, we may not need a hundred-year rotation."

On logging wilderness: "In the Glacier Peak Wilderness there is a billion board feet rotting. It's of no use to anybody. Wilderness is set up with no access. It's a monstrous waste in terms of total public interest. Under sound multiple-use management, one season you could take the crop of trees and open the area. The next season wildlife would flourish and thrive and roads will be made available to people who like to drive. That way everybody would get a piece of the action but when it's wilderness—well, maybe less than one percent of the people have it. Just how much should the public have to sacrifice in terms of natural resources?"

On logging national parks: "Maybe the only way to preserve park values is to manage them. We have to open up the national parks. We're losing millions of trees to fire and beetle infestation. We are underutilizing our national parks."

On erosion from logging: "Obviously there will be some soil damage, but what is going to happen if you don't log? The trees will die of fire or disease."

On logging watersheds: "Even where you cut most drastically along creek beds the impact on fish is short-term. We feel that, if properly handled, clearcutting will have minimal impact. Timber has commercial value. Fish do not. If we don't take the timber we'll lose jobs. If a spawning bed is accidentally hurt, maybe it's more beneficial to society to set up a hatchery."

On the use of pesticides in forestry: "Despite all the exposure of humans and animals to huge dosages of DDT over many years there is no evidence any person has died or suffered from it, and there is little substantial evidence that animal life is really adversely affected."

If one allows himself to believe that most Americans consider logs more important than fish, or that they wish upon the national parks a good, close haircut, then one could come away

from a man like Moshofsky with a terrible sense of hopeless-
ness. Fortunately, most Americans do not share Moshofsky's
cold, businesslike attitude toward trees, and so they do not
indulge in such fantasies.

Outside Georgia-Pacific's shiny new Portland office building stands a sculpture which seems to reflect all the fantasies
emanating from the mouths and typewriters inside. It is a
section of redwood, crosscut and hollowed out. Great spikes
protrude from the trunk. The sculptor intended these to sym-
bolize the rays of the life-giving sun. Instead, they resemble the
deadly points of some gigantic mace. And in the hollow of the
log sits a small redwood in bronze. For what *that* means, use
your imagination. The sculpture—spikes, log, bronze and all
—is called *PERPETUITY*.

Monstrous hoaxes come in all kinds of packages.

8

Everything points to a transfer of the Forest Service: every-thing, that is, except the desire of successive Secretaries of Agri-culture to hang on to a sizable bureaucratic kingdom and the desire of the timber industry to have nothing disturb its com-fortable relations with an agency it has come to know very well.
—*The New York Times,*
editorial, March 9, 1971

Discrediting the Forest Service in the eyes of the public would make it a pushover to move the Forest Service into Interior where preservationists believe they can gain more control. And you would see more commercial timberlands going into wilder-ness and parks.
—Dean Sherman's Forest Industry Affairs letter

8. Toward a New Forest Policy

No single law or policy will bring a halt to the deforestation of America. The old ways do not die so easily. Nor can anyone at this time possibly advance all the solutions to all the problems of forest management and the reasonable distribution of forest land between commercial and wilderness uses. Some partial solutions, however, have been advanced—reorganization of the Forest Service, a temporary moratorium on clearcutting in the national forests and on the export of saw logs, a ream of specific recommendations for improved forest practices. Implemented together, these recommendations could help turn the last page on a sordid chapter in the history of resource mismanagement in America.

(1) *Reorganization*

The Forest Service, mistrusted by conservationists, exploited by industry, and polarized within its own ranks, should be placed under new leadership, new principles, and a new department—a Department of Natural Resources.

In an editorial of March 9, 1971, *The New York Times* pointed out the need for such a department. "The Brownlow Committee," said *The Times,* "recommended it to President Roosevelt in 1937 and a task force of the first Hoover Commission made substantially the same proposal a dozen years later. Now President Nixon has adopted the idea . . . As envisaged by the President's Advisory Council on Executive Organization headed by Roy L. Ash, the new department would consist of four major divisions. The nucleus of each already exists in the Department of the Interior. The opposition arises over the transferring of logically related agencies from other departments . . . The Forest Service now engages in a multitude of activities which exactly parallel those of the companion agencies in Interior. It is a recreation agency with as many visitors as the National Park Service. It manages public land like the Bureau of Land Management. It manages wildlife as does the Bureau of Sport Fisheries and Wildlife. The Ash Council report observes: Common management would enable better planning of timber harvest, location of facilities to meet recreational demands, overhead savings."

To meet all these complex demands, the head of the new Forest Service must be a man plucked not from the existing bureaucracy but from the outside—whether it be a university, the legal profession, or an environmental group. His qualifications should include not only a thorough knowledge of forestry but of ecology, geology, sociology, perhaps even philosophy or law. Clearly, such a leader must give multiple use more than lip service and, with the backing of a strong secretary of the Department of Natural Resources, establish firm regulations for the timber industry. The goals of the new Forest Service should not be to make as much money as possible nor to keep increasing the allowable cut beyond the level which matches growth, no matter how much pressure is put on it to do so. Finally, the

five-million-acre backlog of areas demanding reforestation
should be completed within a reasonable length of time—say
five years—with congressional appropriations an obvious pre-
requisite.

(2) *Moratoriums: Clearcutting and Exports*

Senator Gale McGee's bill (S. 1592) calling for a two-year
moratorium on clearcutting in the national forests should be
passed to allow time for a thorough study. Such a study should
be conducted by an impartial group of citizens, timber industry
representatives, and key Forest Service personnel to determine
what the nation's timber needs really are and just *where* and
how all future logging should be permitted. (Buying time
should also allow the Forest Service to catch up on its backlog
of reforestation projects.) Meanwhile, a second high-level
commission of scientists should determine the full extent of
existing damage by clearcutting—to soil, watersheds, and wildlife—and use the results of such a study to pass federal forestry
laws to assure complete environmental protection. The commission should sort out facts from fiction, and compile case
histories as well as statistics to back its recommendations.
Neither of the study groups referred to above should be a Public
Land Law Review Commission for forests, headed by a powerful congressman who is industry-oriented. If congressional participation is required, then lawmakers such as Church, McGee,
Metcalf, Dingell and Saylor should be included.

The highly questionable policy of exporting logs to Japan
should also fall under a moratorium. Some 2.38 billion board
feet of logs were exported to Japan in 1970—plus enough plywood, pulp and chips to satisfy half of the United States' resi-
dential construction. With an export moratorium, at least,
depletion of America's forests for the benefit of Japan could be
slowed down.

Significant congressional action is not likely in the immediate future. In September, 1971, President Nixon announced the appointment of an advisory panel on timber and the environment, recommended a year earlier by an interagency committee on softwood timber supply. Named as chairman of the panel was Fred Seaton, former secretary of the interior during the Eisenhower administration. Other members are Dr. Stephen Spurr of the University of Texas; Marion Clausen, Resources for the Future; Ralph Hodges, general manager of the National Forest Products Association, and Dr. Donald Zinn of the University of Rhode Island.

The presidential directive to the panel is for a study of the entire range of timber management problems. This would include advice to the president on how to increase the supply of timber to meet growing housing needs while "protecting and enhancing" the quality of the environment. The panel was directed to deliver its report to the president by July 1, 1972.

Many environmentalists regard creation of this study group as a means of sidetracking, at least temporarily, action to correct Forest Service timber management practices and to delay action on legislative proposals such as the McGee moratorium on clearcutting and the Metcalf timber management reform measure. Moreover, existence of this panel almost certainly puts in the deep freeze any presidential action on the proposed executive order to protect de facto wilderness areas.

(3) *Improved Forest Practices*

As far as federal forestry legislation is concerned, the bill introduced by Sen. Lee Metcalf (D.-Mont.) and Rep. John Dingell (D.-Mich.) is an excellent beginning. S.1734 and H.R. 7383, called the National Forest Reforestation Act, would improve practices on public and private lands in the following ways:

• Require that commercial timber harvesting on privately owned lands be conducted by qualified and licensed professional foresters in accordance with forestry plans that give paramount weight to protecting the future productivity of the land, and to sustained yield.

• Provide incentives to private landowners and industry to encourage proper reforestation and adequately long rotations in harvesting.

• Direct the secretary of agriculture to conduct timber harvesting on the national forests in a fashion that accords priority to protection of the natural features and future productivity of the land.

• Protect de facto wilderness in national forest lands by requiring mandatory review under the Wilderness Act of 1964.

Pointing out that the quality of forestry in the United States is low and getting lower, Gordon Robinson, the Sierra Club's forestry consultant, has come up with some specific guidelines. Robinson's "Excellent Forestry," based on his twenty-seven years of experience with sustained yield forestry for the Southern Pacific Company, offers a plan that would preclude typical tree farms and massive clearcutting. He writes:

Excellent forestry has four characteristics, each of which requires considerable elaboration for clear understanding. First of all, cut must be matched with growth— that is to say the amount of timber removed from one's property must not be more than the amount that will grow in the cutting interval. This is generally referred to as sustained yield and where one is working with virgin timber, this means continuous production at an even rate with the aim of achieving at the earliest practicable time an approximate balance between net growth and harvest either by annual or somewhat longer periods.

Excellent forestry also implies growing timber on long rotations, generally speaking I would say from 100 to 200 years. Rotation is the age of trees at the time of cutting plus whatever time is required for reestablishment after logging.

A third characteristic of excellence is selection management in preference to alternative systems such as clearcutting wherever this is consistent with the silvics of the species involved. This implies frequent light cuts, generally not removing more than 10% of the volume at one time. Where clearcutting must be practiced, as in the management of highly intolerant species, the openings should be kept as small as possible, preferably no greater in diameter than half the height of the surrounding timber.

Finally, excellent forestry is characterized by extreme care to avoid damage to the soil, the all-important basic resource.

Excellent forestry costs nothing but restraint and offers the greatest gifts a forest can provide.

(4) *Balancing Uses*

And yet even the best theories of forestry, laws to put the land back together and keep it that way, and plans to give the Forest Service a new name and a new set of rules do not answer the critical question: How much of the national forests should be used for timber production? The following figures represent a general scheme of levels of intensity and are not based on surveys or inventories. They were suggested by Michael McCloskey, executive director of the Sierra Club, to show a fair and approximate way to divvy up the national forest pie.

To begin with there are 186 million acres of national forest, of which 97 million acres are catalogued as commercial forest land.

Fourteen million acres are in wilderness or primitive status, but only two million acres of this total contain commercial timber.

Of the 97 million acres of commercial forest land, another

2 to 3 million acres should be withdrawn and added to the wilderness system. (At least 6 to 8 million acres of national forest land must be added to the wilderness system—but much of it is not wooded.)

After deleting some 3 million acres for wilderness, 94 million acres of commercial forest will be left. Of this, 20 million acres ought to be subject to no more than *modified cuts*—with scenic and recreational values given priority.

That leaves 74 million acres, of which 40 million acres might be cut with *moderate intensity*—but with great precautions to protect highly intermingled multiple-use values.

On the remaining 34 million acres where multiple-use values are lowest and timber values predominate, intensive cutting might occur, but still excellent forestry should be practiced.

Although 34 million acres devoted almost exclusively to timber production seems exorbitant, the Timber Supply Act would have placed *all* 97 million acres under intensive management, using fertilizers and pesticides, guaranteeing the timber industry dominant use.

If such an allocation is to work, there must be new criteria for identifying the areas where intensive management can or should take place. One guideline would be the capability of the land for growing trees. Another would be aesthetic value of the land in question. The so-called "best" land for timber production might be the flat, low slopes of the forests, the least scenic parts, the areas with low game populations, stable soil conditions, and watersheds that can be easily protected.

The designation of 34 million acres for intensive forestry by no means implies that thousand-acre clearcuts can be made at whim. Here, as elsewhere, clearcutting would be in small patches, watersheds protected, and routine checks made on such things as erosion, regeneration, water quality, and fish and wildlife populations.

It is certain that logging will continue on a large scale in the national forests. There will be squabbles as to what areas ought to receive the greatest logging impact, and someone will always find beauty in the most passive patch of woodlands and insist that it not be cut down. Logging, however, *can* be pursued with a sense of stewardship.

The struggle of our time is to maintain abundance and production and yet keep man's inner spirit intact. His search for freedom invariably leads him to the wonders of the wilderness, there to experience the true measure of living and to realize his own time and function on earth. It is in the forest-as-wilderness that man comes to know there is a place in his life for the elk, just as there is for the song of the hermit thrush, the whisper of leaves in the rain, the rise of a salmon in a stream. There would be great emptiness in the land—and in man—if there were no elk to break the stillness of the morning, no golden eagles to wheel against a granite cliff, no Menzies' beardtongue penstemon stubbornly thriving in the high mountain soils. Small things these are, yet essential to man's well-being, all part of his need to pass on to future generations an untrammeled part of the forest. As Aldo Leopold once wrote, "The chance to find a pasque flower is a right as inalienable as free speech."

The chance to find an untouched forest is our right, too.

We must learn to care as easily as we have learned to destroy.

Epilogue

While government officials and politicians presented their own cases in Portland in August 1971 at a Senate subcommittee hearing on the Hatfield and McGee forest bills, veteran Oregon logger Bob Ziak made his own plea. It follows verbatim.

My name is Bob Ziak. I am a clear cut high lead logger.

I was born in Astoria, Oregon, fifty-four years ago. My father was a logger. My mother took me from the hospital to a logging camp to live. The forests are my life.

At first the timber was virgin, production was tremendous, there were no controls and the resulting destruction and waste was appalling.

I've clear cut to the edge of a river, destroyed priceless streams, found jewel-like lakes within our cutting lines and left them as ugly holes staring into the skies.

I've seen the eagle tree left standing all alone only to see the birds leave and the tree die because each needed a stand in order to survive.

I helped log thousands of clear cuts, saw the animals move in and then come under a murderous cross-fire from hunters on the network of roads, with no place in sight to go in their terror-stricken flight.

I am deeply concerned about our forests. They are disappearing—from 600 years of age to 35. Man planted in solid blocks, tree farming if you wish, but our forests are going, going, gone.

Detach yourselves from this earth and look down on us from the heavens above. Gentlemen, this is all there is. There is no more and the time is running out.

Note

The September 1971 issue of *Reader's Digest* contained a twenty-page supplement entitled "What Are We Doing About Our Environment?" which featured self-effacing backpats from notorious polluters. The page devoted to "what the timber industry is doing" was paid for by the American Forest Institute—chief supporter of the Timber Supply Bill and industry's major public relations bugle. Among its claims:

We still have 75% as much forestland as we did when Columbus landed.

... We have more trees now than in 1950.

... Wood is an endlessly renewable resource.

The demand for wood is growing faster than old-fashioned forestry is growing trees.

Fully one-third (250 million acres) is unproductive or set aside in parks and wilderness areas.

Here (state and federal forests) is where modern forest management can do the most to improve our timber supply—without endangering the forest . . .

The truth is that in 1492 logging was yet to be inflicted upon a continent whose virgin forests covered most of its land mass. Today there is only about 10 percent (not 75 percent) as much forestland as when Columbus stepped ashore.

With the Forest Service now more than five million acres behind in reforestation—more than at any time during its history—and industry lagging to an even greater extent, there *cannot* be more trees than there were in 1950.

Wood is *not* an endlessly renewable resource—as vast clearcut areas that have failed to regenerate clearly demonstrate.

The demand for wood is *not* growing faster than old-fashioned forestry grows trees. (See earlier text.)

With national parks totaling 14.275 million acres, national wilderness totaling 10.1 million acres, national monuments comprising 9.8 million acres and such "unproductive" areas as national military parks, battlefields, historic sites, memorials, and cemeteries totaling about 125,000 acres, the 250 million acres that the timber industry calls "unproductive" or "set aside" is unrealistic, unless one includes national parkways (130 thousand acres), seashores (231.7 thousand acres), and the 89 million acres of national forest not open to commercial timber production. In any case, all of the above account for only half of what industry alleges is being shielded from its chain saws.

Acknowledgments

During the writing of this book, scores of people from all parts of the country contributed countless hours to my understanding of the subject. I cannot name them all. There are some, however, who deserve special recognition for what they have done to help this book along.

One such individual is Gordon Robinson, forestry consultant for the Sierra Club, who was patient in explaining to me the nitty-gritty facts of forestry and who researched much of my material. My thanks to Mike McCloskey of the Sierra Club for lending me his wide knowledge. Constance Stallings, assistant editor of Sierra Club Books, covered in depth the second round of the Church hearings. In Seattle, I had the support of Brock Evans, the attorney-conservationist, to whom this book is dedicated for his gallant efforts in the fight to save the forests.

In Oregon, I had the help and hospitality of Dr. and Mrs. Sanford Tepfer of Eugene and their three sons—Gary, Fred and Mark, who not only showed me the forests but also shared their particular enthusiasm for them. In Steamboat, I stayed with Mr. and Mrs. Frank Moore at their haven along the Umpqua River. Their hospitality sustained me for many days while touring the devastated Umpqua National Forest with rangers as well as loggers. In Portland, Larry Williams, executive director of the Oregon Environmental Council was my host and guide through the Olympic Peninsula, the Gifford Pinchot National Forest, the Coast Range and the rain forest.

In northern California, Dave Van de Mark of Trinidad spent almost a week introducing me to his redwood country— the lovely parks as well as the ugly logged areas. The magic of Redwood Creek which we floated down in a raft will remain with me always.

In the eastern part of the country, there were many who were helpful at the three-day Church hearings—witnesses from every part of the United States who gave me their viewpoints, their research material, and most of all, their time. Among these were Dean Arnold Bolle who authored the controversial "Bolle Report" on the Bitterroot National Forest and to whom special thanks is given for allowing me to quote extensively from this very important document; Dr. Robert Curry who astounded the committee with his findings on soil depletion; Dr. Charles Wharton of Georgia State University who gave me much-needed biological background; Douglas Scott of The Wilderness Society; Michael Frome of *Field and Stream;* and Jim Risser of the *Des Moines Register* who shared his well-documented series of reports on the Bitterroots. In Washington, Mr. and Mrs. Lloyd Tupling were gracious hosts. In Richwood, West Virginia, Lawrence and Howard Deitz and Bob Smith were among the dozens of residents of that delightful town who helped to make my stay pleasant as well as informative.

In Colorado, my long-time friends in the conservation field were of inestimable help. Roger Hansen of the Rocky Mountain Center on Environment provided me with copies of his own research, gave me access to his files, and firm support in the completion of this task, particularly the section on PLLRC. Boyd Norton of The Wilderness Society sent me clippings and mapped out places to go and people to see. My thanks also to Kay Collins of the Denver Conservation Library for allowing me to borrow special reference material and for digging up some facts I had missed.

I had some exciting hours with Jim Roush of Seattle who flew me over hundreds of miles of clearcuts in the Coast Range and in the Cascades. In Eugene, I saw one of many examples of a concerned and conscientious Forest Service in Zane Grey Smith, the new supervisor of the Willamette National Forest.

The timber industry was at all times gracious, gallant and patient with me, even though we did not agree on most issues. The leading example of industry courtesy was Boise Cascade. In Boise, Rich Kettlewell arranged my schedule for me—in Idaho as well as Oregon where Ed Kupillas spent a day showing me some of Boise Cascade's Coast Range forests. I found Bill Moshofsky of Georgia-Pacific to be honest, direct and a delightful luncheon companion. At Weyerhaeuser, George Hess took my unexpected arrival in his stride and gave me his day, enlivened by Bernie Orell's brief appearance. Other industry men—James Quigley of U.S. Plywood-Champion Papers, Kirt Ewart of Boise Cascade and George Craig of Western Lumber Manufacturers presented their side of the story to me "without jibes."

Finally, I offer a medal of honor to my secretary Coral O'Brien who waded through stacks of reference material, illegible handwriting, and finally finished the typing of this manuscript from her hospital bed. To my friends, Mara Soudakoff, Linda Collins and Bud Baker, some recognition ought to be given for holding me together during some very long and difficult months.

—Nancy Wood
Colorado Springs
September, 1971

Other Sierra Club Battlebooks

Energy A Crisis in Power, by John Holdren and Philip Herrera. 256 pages. $2.75

America's appetite for energy—and particularly for electric power—is voracious. Some resource planners predict the production of power will continue to double every ten years just to meet the demand. But at what cost to the U.S. environment when fossil fuels pollute the air, hydropower plants destroy rivers, and the "nukes" pose hazards that continue to be debated in every nuke-served community?

Energy explores this dilemma on two levels. First, a scientist examines the sources and consumption of energy in the U.S. and describes how the production of power inevitably leaves its mark upon the environment. Then a journalist takes over, reporting on the remarkable efforts of concerned citizens to protect the environment from the ravages of power-triggered air, water and landscape pollution. Together, their observations raise hope that the U.S. *can* find a rational solution to its energy crisis.

Oilspill by Wesley Marx.   144 pages. $2.75

In 1970, an estimated 1.5 billion gallons of crude and bunker oil spilled into the oceans of the world from tankers and offshore wells. Nearly half of the major spills were within a mile of the shore. The toll in shellfish and seabirds, in lost recreational opportunities along miles of gummy beaches, in direct economic setbacks to the coastal communities affected will never be fully tabulated.

Oilspill reveals the full story of this increasing threat to our precious marine environments. Author Wesley Marx describes the ecological impact of spilt oil, the vulnerability of supertankers, the hazards of coastal refineries, the flaws in our fumbling technology for cleaning up after industry's mess. Marx also explores some new ideas that could help ease America off her hydrocarbon habit before the oceans are irrevocably fouled and oil replaces water as the most prominent fluid on this planet.

Oil On Ice by Tom Brown.   160 pages. $1.95

One of Alaska's foremost journalists explores a leading threat to the delicate ecosystem of our largest state, as the proposed oil pipeline controversy nears a final decision. The extraction of petroleum here might well inject new strength into Alaska's economy but it could just as easily upset the arctic's fragile environment if scalding oil is piped 800 miles from the North Slope to Valdez, over and under unstable permafrost soils and across earthquake fault zones. Brown presents his information objectively, leaving conclusions to the reader.

Mercury by Katherine and Peter Montague.   160 pages. $2.25

A startling, fresh account of how U.S. public health officials looked the other way while quicksilver infiltrated the food chains leading to man. As *The Los Angeles Times* noted: "The Montagues have written a sane, balanced and well-documented history... Its value is enhanced by the excellent end-of-the-book listings of polluters, polluting processes, state and federal legislation and a bibliography. Well worth the time of anyone concerned with the facts behind a current scare."

About the Sierra Club

The Sierra Club, founded in 1892 by John Muir, has consistently devoted itself to the study and protection of America's scenic resources and wild places. Sierra Club publications are part of the nonprofit effort the club carries on as a public trust. There are chapters in all parts of the United States. Participation is invited in the club's program to enjoy and preserve wilderness, wildlife, and a quality environment for all men, for all time.

Part of the club program aims to service the growing student environmental movement on the nation's campuses. Information on organizational techniques, eco-tactics and community action is available from The Campus Program, Sierra Club, Mills Tower, San Francisco, California 94104.

The Sierra Club
Mills Tower
San Francisco, California 94104

Please enroll me as a member of the Sierra Club:

Name_____

Address_____

City, state, zip_____

Dues: $5 admission, plus $15 (regular membership) , $7.50 (spouse) or $5 (full-time students, age 15 through 23) .

I enclose_____